G000140907

Murder at the Masked Ball

Murder at the Masked Ball

The assassination of Gustaf III of Sweden

GARDAR SAHLBERG

translated from the Swedish by
Paul Britten Austin

MACDONALD · LONDON

Den aristokratiska ligan first published by Bonniers, 1969
This translation first published in Great Britain in 1974 by
Macdonald and Jane's (Macdonald and Co. (Publishers) Ltd),
St Giles House, 49 Poland Street
London W.1

SBN 356 03590 5

Made and printed in Great Britain by
REDWOOD BURN LIMITED
Trowbridge & Esher

CONTENTS

LIST OF ILLUSTRATIONS

Central Stockholm in the 18th Century

1. The Opera (not built when map was drawn)
2. The Royal Palace
3. Blasieholmen
4. Gamla Kungsholmsbrogatan
5. The Stream
6. To the North Barrier, Solna, Haga, Huvudasta and Gavle
7. The Haymarket
8. Drottninggatan
9. Bollhus Theatre on Slottsbacken
10. Riddarholmen
11. House of Nobles and Riddarhustorget
12. The Artillery Barracks
13. The Slaughterhouse Bridge
14. The North Bridge (not built when map was drawn)
15. Helgeandsholmen
16. Baggensgatan
17. St. Nicholas Church, Storkyrkobrinken and Trangsund
18. Munkbron
19. Fredsgatan
20. Norrmalmstorg (today Gustav Adolfs Torg)
21. Mynttorget
22. St. James' Church
23. Malmskillnadsgatan
24. Kastanhof
25. Regeringsgatan
26. "Soder"–the South Side
27. The Sluice Bridges
28. Kornhamnstorg
29. Klara Sodra Kyrkogatan
30. Gotgatan
31. To Skanstull barrier and Gallows Hill
32. Lejonbacken
33. Skeppsholmen naval base
34. Packartorget
35. Arsenalsgatan (today Hamngatan).
36. Smedjegarden and prison
37. Skeppsbron Quay
38. The Harbour
39. Ladugardslandet, today Ostermalm
40. Lake Malaren

I

GENERAL PECHLIN LOOKS YOUNG AGAIN

Far out on the little island of Blasieholmen in the middle of Stockholm, close to the timber bridge over to Skeppsholmen, there once stood an old palace. Its main façade overlooked the narrow channel known as the Stream, and like many of Stockholm's aristocratic houses it had two wings. These reached out on either side of its courtyard at the rear, towards the narrow street. Like other nobles' houses whose arrogant roofs overtopped the straggling tangle of single-storey houses, taverns and brothels along the shore, its walls were whitewashed.

One evening just before Christmas 1791, some carriages with liveried footmen came driving up to the wrought-iron gate in the wall connecting the two wings. Above the gate a crown and the owner's initials proclaimed that he was a nobleman – a *friherre* – a count. All the gentlemen who entered the building also bore aristocratic names. One was Magnus Brahe, the premier count of Sweden. He was accompanied by his brother-in-law Count Claes Lewenhaupt and by Baron Adolf Ludwig Stierneld. In fact, it had been Count Brahe who had summoned these two gentlemen to the capital. The other guests bore names just as illustrious, or else were men who had made their mark by boldly opposing the king's policies at recent *riksdags* – assemblies of the Swedish parliament. Here came the wealthy barons Charles and Louis de Geer from Leufsta; an equerry, Bogislaus Staël von Holstein, who held a position in the National Debt Office; and a master of the royal household, Henrik Jakob von Düben.

The palace's aged owner and their host this evening was

Major-General Carl Fredrik Pechlin. He had invited them to come and have a chat – the rumours of another *riksdag* had been flying about for some time now, and had just been confirmed. For the aristocratic party such worrying news made consultations imperative. Pechlin, deeply experienced in politics and a most cagey old gentleman, had taken care to time his invitation for the exact hour when the king and court were on their way to the Opera: at such an hour these discussions on nearby Blasieholmen would attract less attention.

A *riksdag* was indispensable. But this time things must not be allowed to turn out as they had at the last stormy *riksdag*, in 1789. Then Gustaf III had arrested nineteen members of the aristocracy and by his Act of Union and Security imposed a virtual dictatorship. At that time Brahe, Pechlin, Charles de Geer and Stierneld had all been deprived of their liberty. Some, it is true, had merely been placed under house-arrest; but others had been exposed to the humiliation of real imprisonment. Since then the opposition had grown in strength. This time it looked as if those of them who – in French-revolutionary style – were calling themselves 'patriots' would be strong enough to resist the king's demands.

Why were they so dissatisfied?

Mostly, the roots of the trouble went back to Gustaf's feckless war against Russia. It was only some eighteen months since it had come to an end. The king's surprise victory at Svensksund, it is true, had rescued the nation from ignominious defeat: and at Värälä, in Finland, an honourable peace had been signed with the Empress Catherine II. Sweden had not been humiliated by being obliged to cede any of her territories to Russia. But the State's finances had been left in parlous plight. The bill for the war had amounted to considerably more than the ten million riksdaler allocated by the previous *riksdag*. This had forced the newly re-established National Debt Office to issue interest-bearing bonds, and these, failing to yield any interest, had drifted out into the money-market as ordinary banknotes, albeit of lower value than those issued by the Bank of Sweden. These 'tail coats', as they were called, proved impossible to cash and were swamping the country. Once again, after the monetary reforms of the earlier and happier part of Gustaf III's reign, Sweden was embarrassed with a double currency; a most troublesome circumstance for all debtors who, when repaying their debts in 'tail coats', were sometimes obliged to fork out as much as sixteen per cent above the nominal sum. Taxes, too, had risen. And likewise the price of all necessary commodities.

But the aristocrats had many other worries, too. What events had they not witnessed in the past six months? What rumours! Some so incredible, people would have stopped their ears and refused to credit them, had it not been for the undoubted trustworthiness of their informants.

These plans, for instance, for suppressing the French Revolution by force of arms and restoring Louis XVI to all his former powers. The project had begun to take shape last summer, when Gustaf III, allegedly for reasons of health, had been staying at Aachen in Germany, and there fallen in with some French émigré nobles who had appealed for his help. Gustaf had placed high hopes in the French royal family's abortive flight from France at midsummer; he had even been intending to meet King Louis and Queen Marie Antoinette at the frontier. The flight, ably planned by the young Swedish count, Hans Axel von Fersen, had been clumsily executed by the chief actors and their great unwieldy *berline* had only got as far as Varennes. But now, where Marie Antoinette's favourite, the tall good-looking Fersen, had failed, Gustaf III was going to succeed by other means. He was dreaming of placing himself at the head of an army recruited by every monarchy in Europe, and from a Sweden already exhausted by his Finnish war had generously offered a contingent of sixteen thousand men.

To come from the monarch of a sparsely populated Scandinavian country, these were flighty projects. And indeed, neither the Emperor, in Vienna, nor the King of Prussia, in Berlin, were really taking him seriously. In September 1791, when Louis XVI had confirmed the new French constitution, he had even received the acclamations of the Paris mob, and people were telling themselves that the tremendous political storm had already blown itself out. But Gustaf III was nothing if not a man of imagination, and now that imagination had taken flight. Driven by his loathing for Jacobinism, he was seeking other means of accomplishing his designs. Perhaps the Swedish and Russian fleets, so recently locked in a life-and-death struggle with each other, could undertake a fraternal expedition, land troops in royalistic Normandy, and the troops march on Paris? The Russian empress had taken a certain interest in this scheme, but had gradually come to the conclusion that autumn was now too far advanced for so risky a nautical enterprise. But at least Gustaf III and Catherine II were now on friendly terms. In October their letters, flying to and fro, had led to the signing of an eight-year treaty of peace and mutual defence between Sweden and Russia. Under this treaty Sweden was to receive an annual subsidy of three hundred thousand roubles. No despicable sum, to be sure. But it would not go far towards solving the imminent financial crisis. A victorious campaign against Paris, on the other hand, might improve Sweden's economic situation: naturally Louis XVI, out of gratitude for such timely aid, would also have to subsidize the Swedish treasury. These plans for invading France, perhaps, could be implemented some time in the spring.

Many Swedish aristocrats – and it was chiefly in aristocratic circles that dissatisfaction was running high – could not swallow the king's overtures to Russia. No sooner had the treaty of friendship been signed than a rumour began to go the rounds that what Catherine was now proposing was a marriage in the near future between the young Swedish

Crown Prince, Gustaf Adolf – as yet no more than thirteen years old – and a Russian archduchess. Supposing the archduchess turned out to be a masculine piece of work – as Russian duchesses so often were? Might she not influence her sickly, none-too-gifted spouse and turn him into a despot?

This double threat of a new bloody war on the one hand, and a royal match with a dynasty decidedly *non grata* in Sweden on the other, had opened up terrifying prospects for the future. The rumours, of course, might be exaggerated. What was already beyond all exaggeration, and an irrefutable fact, was the desperate financial state of affairs. And here the aristocracy were afraid that the king, by a *coup* at the now imminent *riksdag*, might seize the assets of the Riksens ständers bank – the Bank of the Estates of the Realm. So far these funds had eluded his grasp. And the Bank of the Estates was the very cornerstone of the country's economy. Horrible rumours were going about that in the event of his encountering strong opposition from the First Estate, the king would quite simply introduce a new, British-style constitution such as once and for all would mean the end of the Swedish aristocracy.

The 'patriots' were agreed. At all costs an effective opposition must be organized. But who should lead it? During the explosive days of the 1789 *riksdag* it had been Field-Marshal Count Fredrik Axel von Fersen – father of 'tall Fersen', Marie Antoinette's friend and lover – who had led the opposition. But that *grand seigneur* – the king had once called him his only worthy opponent – was now seventy-three and was refusing blankly to engage himself in a revolution the necessity of which was everywhere being urged by the young aristocratic hotheads. In fact, so far from inciting anyone to revolution, Fersen was doing the very opposite: he was advising everyone to keep calm. For his part he was not even going to attend the *riksdag*. Some other leader, therefore, would have to be found. There was only one man in whose leadership the patriots had sufficient confidence – Pechlin, the old gentleman on Blasieholmen.

He, too, was old, of course – almost as old as Fersen. All his great triumphs as a political whip and unmatched political intriguer had been celebrated ages ago. During the frantic party struggles of the Age of Freedom Pechlin had unscrupulously and incessantly changed sides, as had best suited his own interests. He had been a pro-French 'Hat' one day and a pro-English 'Cap' the next. When Gustaf, shortly after his accession to the throne, had seized power in 1772 Pechlin had withdrawn to his Småland farms and ironworks to devote his energies to the modernization of agriculture, where his success had made him one of the biggest landowners and ironmasters in all Sweden. But now he was a widower, and was back in Stockholm, living in his great house on Blasieholmen. Short of stature, rather plump and bent of back, he had a chubby face and lively eyes which blinked incessantly. In his old age Pechlin had become weak and infirm, suffered from chronic colds and prolapsed haemorrhoids, and was seldom seen about the town. But age had not blunted the swiftness of his intellect, or dulled the quickness of his repartee or his sardonic sense of humour. Nor had it crippled his will to oppose that 'sovereignty principle' – established by the earlier Vasa Kings, suppressed during the age of Freedom, now re-established by Gustaf III and so utterly detested by the Swedish aristocracy.

And now Pechlin, with lively gestures and many highly-coloured expressions, was presenting his political programme to his guests. He made no bones about his radicalism.

During recent years the national debt had risen from eight to thirty million, and now the country was on the very verge of bankruptcy. Could anyone doubt that, as long as the reins of power lay in the hands of a despot, this crazy sort of government would go on?

These were bold, revolutionary words. After enjoying their good dinner, Pechlin's guests were only too happy to listen to them. In every way they were prepared to help him fight the royal authority. Three hours later they took leave of their host, where he stood in the porchway. No one who was in the know could have guessed that this hospitable house, whose owner was laughing and waving his guests off with witty sallies, had been the scene of anything but the most innocent of supper parties. But the chief of the city police, Henrik Liljensparre, had his spies everywhere. Next day, in his report to the king, he listed not only the names of all those who had taken part in the conference, but its exact duration. And added: 'Cautious they are in the highest degree, and more than reticent. General Pechlin, old as he is, seems young again.'

Just what information Pechlin had confided to his guests that evening, however, the chief of police was never to know. And it is also possible that in the course of his conversation with them Pechlin never actually revealed that plan, which, though still only a vague mirage, when finally implemented would make possible the change of regime they all so desired; a plan which, as fate would have it, had been brought to Pechlin's ears by a person who had been living for a couple of years on his very doorstep.

The wings of his great house on Blasieholmen contained a number of apartments, and these the general was in the habit of letting out. With the wheelmaker and the farrier who lived there he cannot have had much contact: but all the more with certain others among his tenants, and more especially with a certain district judge, by name Anders Nordell. Nordell, too, belonged to the opposition. Aggressively so. If he had not had the sense to steer clear of the city during the 1789 *riksdag*, he too would certainly have been arrested. In the autumn of that year he had moved into an apartment in Pechlin's house, and, having helped his landlord in certain legal matters, thereafter enjoyed the privilege of dining uninvited at the general's dinner table. Usually that table was laid for some eight or ten such unbidden guests. Nordell, flattered by this standing invitation, had taken advantage of it about once a week. And sometimes he would drop in on the general to smoke a pipe of tobacco with him, or to drink a glass of small-beer together, while they thumbed through the pages of certain German newspapers to which Pechlin subscribed. These newspapers came by the Friday post, and Nordell was not the only person who came out to Blasieholmen to read about their French friends' thrilling struggle against an insufferable despotism. Many other officials and officers were no less curious than Nordell. So long as their intentions were honest and straightforward they were equally welcome.

Anders Nordell was a restless middle-aged man. For the last thirteen years he had been serving as district judge out at Vallentuna, some ten or twelve miles north of the city. The inhabitants of Vallentuna were always going to law with one another, and they often turned to Nordell – who knew his way about in the tangled thickets of the law – to protect their interests. One of his clients, more especially, had so often applied to him for help, they had come to be on really friendly terms. A former captain of the First Life Guards, who – after being dismissed the service – had rented a farm out in his native parish of Vallentuna and there had set up as a farmer, albeit with questionable success. His name: Jakob Johan Anckarström. Hard, mean, always involved in disputes, Anckarström did not care who knew his political opinions. And on a recent visit to Gotland – the big Swedish island in the middle of the Baltic – he had got himself into really hot water.

Nordell had had things to relate about that trip of Anckarström's which had gradually caused the old fox Pechlin to prick up his ears. Nordell was himself to have gone with Anckarström to Gotland, but had been prevented at the last moment. Now he was thanking his lucky stars he had not got mixed up in that wretched business. This was how it had happened.

Early in August 1790, Captain Anckarström, together

with his wife and a close friend of the family, vice-auditor Barthold Runeberg, had sailed over to Gotland on a small cargo boat. They were going to take a look at certain lands which the captain was considering buying. For his part Runeberg was to visit some relatives.

'Even on the voyage over,' Nordell had informed Pechlin, 'they spoke so insultingly about the king's disastrous way of waging war that the other passengers were shocked.'

'Of waging war?' objected Pechlin. 'Was that before peace was signed at at Värälä, then?'

'Negotiations were going on,' Nordell replied. 'But of that, of course, they knew nothing. On the contrary, everyone believed the Russian battle fleet – still stronger than the Swedish fleet, even after 9 July and the battle of Svenskssund – was about to attack Gotland. Arriving in port at Kyllej, the travellers took accommodation in the house of a certain Skipper Olof Unérus. There they went on painting the future in the most dismal colours, particularly as it was likely to concern people living out there, on the island's east coast. Their words reached other ears. A coastguards inspector, taking Anckarström for a spy, jumped to the conclusion that Runeberg, who is a native of Gotland, could only be his guide. In his report to the military commander on the island he accused them of insulting both king and army, and of saying that the victory thanksgiving had had no other purpose than to pull the wool over the eyes of the simple-minded mob. Yes, Anckarström was even said to have told the skipper that if he wanted his dog to be promoted to the rank of ensign then he should send it over to Finland . . . '

After that the mills of the law had begun to grind, albeit slowly, with their usual deliberation. Brought before Visby City Court, Runeberg had denied the accusation. Thereafter the two men had been allowed to return to Stockholm. The acting Chancellor of Justice, Låstbom, however, had decided that the case should come up for trial. So, in October 1790, they were ordered to appear again before the court in Visby, and there answer for their abusive utterances. By this time, however, Anckarström was no longer living in Vallentuna, but had moved back into Stockholm with his family. He had brought with him a few cows, to sell milk.

A stormy autumn voyage across the Baltic was certainly not a very attractive prospect; but what terrified them most of all was the charge: high treason. By presenting suitable doctor's certificates it should have been possible to get their appearance before the Visby court adjourned until the following spring. But the office of the Governor of Stockholm had intervened. Under police escort Anckarström and Runeberg were taken over to Visby, and when finally the hearings came to an end – they had lasted a whole month – and all the documents in the case had been sent back to the Svea Court of Appeal in Stockholm for judgment, the two men were still forbidden to leave the island. Such insolent and high-handed treatment had still further embittered them against the authorities.

The sequel had been no less humiliating. After a reluctant four-month stay on Gotland, the accused – still under police escort – had been sent back to Stockholm, and there set at liberty, but confined to their houses. Not until November 1791 had Anckarström been allowed to go out.

'And the sentence?'

'None has ever been passed. It's said the king wants to keep Anckarström on tenterhooks . . . . But over his swarthy head hangs, like a Damocles sword, a sentence of death for high treason. If the rumour is true, that is, that the king wants things that way.'

True or false, the rumour was of no great importance in Pechlin's eyes. It was the story as a whole that had excited his imagination. A dismissed captain, violent and rough by nature and blinded with hatred – here was an acquaintance worth making! Pechlin wished to know more about this nobleman; and during his repeated visits, Nordell, who was deeply in Pechlin's confidence, had been able to tell him more about Anckarström. He was married to a wealthy wife, Gustaviana Elisabeth Löwen, an officer's daughter, with whom he had a number of young children. Last Michaelmas he had moved into a house owned by Peter Fernström, a merchant captain. It lay between Drottninggatan and Klara Lake.

The house stood at the north-west corner of Gamla Kungsholmsbrogatan and Målargatan. For his family Captain Anckarström had rented a third-floor apartment. For his own part, he mostly lived in a little barely-furnished room at the back of the building. His marriage could hardly be called happy. His wife was a hard-natured, mannish woman. Recently, the marriage had gone even more grievously on the rocks. Anckarström had found out that Runeberg, his good friend and fellow-traveller on his trips to Gotland, was his wife's lover. Yet he felt he could not do without her. After all, she had brought a respectable amount of capital into their estate, and this had enabled him to increase his fortune as a money-lender. On himself Anckarström lavished few of the good things of life. Whenever his wife went to see her relatives in the country and the two maidservants came to him for housekeeping money, he was always extremely tight-fisted.

In the flat beneath the Anckarströms' lived two young ladies, Ulrika and Catharina Linnerhjelm. From time to time they received visits from their sister and her husband, Count Claes Horn, of Huvudsta. Because of the young ladies' association with the Anckarströms, Jakob Johan Anckarström had become acquainted with Horn. Before long he had told Horn of the charge of *crimen laesae majestatis* against him. Nor did he beat about the bush. He hated the king – a hatred due not merely to the injustices personally suffered by himself, but to the entire nation's sufferings under heavy taxes and general misgovernment. Count Horn's own economy happened to be rather strained, so when Anckarström offered him a loan, he was grateful to accept it. Their friendship was confirmed.

All these matters Nordell was able to tell Pechlin about

during his visits, as they sat there sucking at their pipes and drinking small-beer. The general gave a contented little smile. Several times since the day when Nordell had first awakened his interest in this cashiered and rebellious captain, he had invited him to his house, and it had been at Pechlin's instigation that the sea captain's new tenant had sought the acquaintance of Claes Horn. Fate sometimes manages things in the most admirable manner.

It had been thanks to the circumstance of Nordell's living in Pechlin's palace that the general had come to know of Anckarström's existence. And now fate had so arranged matters that Anckarström happened to be a neighbour to the Misses Linnerhjelm, in whose apartment, without anyone suspecting what they were up to, he could discuss matters with the like-minded Claes Horn. Pechlin had thought Anckarström a rather insignificant person, crude and uneducated. If Claes Horn, with his famous name, his brilliant gifts and his revolutionary sympathies, attached himself to him, a simple act of revenge could be made to wear the aspect of a sublime deed of patriotism. Perhaps one or more persons should be added from the group of activists with whom Pechlin was more closely connected. At least one of them would do perfectly. Pechlin did not move in the same circles as the Horn family, neither the young count of Huvudsta, nor his old father, General Fredrik Horn. True, Pechlin was closely related to the latter by marriage; but during the last years of the Age of Freedom the two generals, Horn and Pechlin, had belonged to opposite political camps; and when, after Gustaf III's *coup d'état* of 1772, Pechlin had been court-martialled for his resistance, Fredrik Horn had been one of the severest judges. Such actions are not easily forgotten; and although both were now of the same opinion – that the time was ripe for a new revolution to revive the country's liberties – the old resentment still simmered. But now, first and foremost, it was the imminent *riksdag* which demanded his attention.

II

JUST GIVE ME THE OPPORTUNITY, AND I'LL DO IT

In the middle of Christmas week, the small Baltic trading port of Gävle, where the masts of many ships frozen up in its harbour pointed up at leaden skies, was shaken out of its winter slumber. A great honour was to be accorded to the little town. In gratitude for its fidelity during the late war it was to be the scene of the *riksdag* now being summoned. Immediately, preparations were set on foot. Thought out in every detail, they clearly revealed the guiding hand of the king himself, that master of theatrical staging. But could the governor of the province, Count Cronstedt, be counted on to implement them? Certainly not. So, right in the midst of his Christmas celebrations, he received urgent orders to betake himself to Stralsund in Swedish Pomerania, whose administration had drifted into a state of bankruptcy. Cronstedt, certainly, was the right man for the task; but the main reason, even so, was that he was out of favour at court and must be moved from Gävle. In his absence the royalist governor of Dalarna, Johan Magnus of Nordin, was to rule from Gävle Castle. And he went to his work with a will.

Gävle in those days must have had some five thousand inhabitants. Now, all of a sudden, its population was to be swelled with about a thousand members of parliament, plus an equal number of servants, clerks, police officers and such of the military as might be required. Every room in the town was inventoried, valued by the magistrates, and thereafter allocated by the police. Little attention was paid to personal preferences, but much to a person's estate and political sympathies. For the separate sessions of the Four Estates – the Nobles, Clergy, Burghers and Peasants – suitable rooms were available; but there was no building large enough to seat a plenum. Governor Nordin therefore ordered all the soldiers of the Hälsingland Regiment out into the forest to fell and chop timber, and in three weeks, despite severe cold and gales, a Hall of State of planks and half-timbers was erected on the east side of the castle. For his Majesty's greater convenience the two buildings were joined by a covered way. Naturally, king and court were to live in the castle. And now royal favours began to be showered on Gävle and its inhabitants. To secure the necessaries of life for the duration of the *riksdag* its citizens were excused all customs dues on foodstuffs, hay, straw, and firewood.

No one really believed the king had chosen Gävle just because he delighted to honour the little town. That was only a pretext. The real reason was that the *riksdag* had to be held at a convenient distance from Stockholm, whose civil service and regiments were all riddled with intriguers. Even the Stockholm burghers, loyal though they had been to the king during the war, were showing signs of dissatisfaction at rising taxation, and some had even begun to feel attracted to Pechlin's camp.

On the eve of the elections both sides – government and the aristocracy – began a violent agitation. The aristocratic party was determined to drum up as many patriots as possible to go to Gävle and thus secure a majority in the First Estate. This move the government countered by decreeing that only *capita* – the actual head of each noble family – were to enjoy an absolute right to attend. All other aristocratic delegates had to obtain special permission, and in this way could be sifted as the government thought best. Reasons could always be found for refusing a permit. On various pretexts unreliable officers were suddenly ordered to remote garrison towns.

One day in the new year, 1792, Anckarström and Horn had a meeting. This time their conversation was not about past wrongs, but about the troubles they could expect at

Gävle.

'Too bad we can't get rid of the king,' said Anckarström, in his Uppland dialect.

'No use wasting thought on that,' said Horn. 'Nothing can be done *encore*.'

'And why on earth not?' exploded Anckarström. 'Just give me an opportunity, and I'll do it.'

Horn's weak nature shrank from violent deeds and he was disturbed by a certain sharpness in Anckarström's tone of voice. Noticing this, Anckarström mumbled something about perhaps being able to kidnap the king out at Haga. Horn greedily swallowed the bait. It was exactly the sort of adventure that appealed to him. With the help of a few men of action, he fancied, they should be able to force an entry at some moment when the king was alone on the ground floor of his little pavilion. After which they could swiftly abduct him and keep him hidden away somewhere until the revolution was accomplished, Gustaf had been deposed, and the crown prince placed on the throne in his stead.

Anckarström assured him his suggestion had not been serious. If too many were implicated in the scheme, it would be impossible to keep it secret. One evening, nevertheless, they drove out to Haga, on the northern outskirts of the city, and under cover of darkness crept up close to the pavilion, whose tall French windows gave them a good view of all that was happening within. To their amazement they saw the king lying on a sofa, a mass of books scattered all round him, clad in a powder-coat, his face so pale and immobile he almost seemed to be dead. Seized with panic, Horn rushed back to the horses waiting for them a short distance away. Anckarström, who had brought a pistol, swore silently and let it slip back into his inside pocket. The Count of Huvudsta, he saw, was not likely to be much use in any enterprise requiring a steady hand and a cool head.

It was at this point that fate again intervened. This time it brought the right man on to the stage. During the week after

Twelfth Night, in the crowded market place, Claes Horn bumped into a friend of his youth: Count Adolf Ludvig Ribbing. Ribbing was on his way to the Gävle *riksdag* and had just arrived in Stockholm. Some years ago, in a moment of passionate indignation, he had resigned his commission as captain of Life Guards and had since been living with his mother Eva Helena Ribbing on her estate at Sjöholm, in Södermanland, south of the capital.

Horn and Ribbing had known each other for twenty years, so their meeting was a hearty one. In his impulsive way Ribbing, his head full only of the forthcoming *riksdag*, tried to talk his friend into coming with him. Ribbing was only twenty-seven, a couple of years younger than Horn, but young though he was, had already made a name for himself as a hot-headed man of the opposition at the last *riksdag*, when he had loudly demanded the instant release of the aristocrats illegally arrested by the king – the more vigorously because one of them, Baron Gustaf Maclean, was his mother's lover and his own patron and protector. But Claes Horn, it seemed, had no desire to leave his wife, with whom he was very much in love, or his young children.

'There's nothing to be done at Gävle, anyway,' he said, despondently.

'The whole nation are nothing but a lot of slaves, tyrannically ruled over by the king. As long as he lives, there can be no freedom for us.'

'I agree with you,' said Ribbing. 'We've lost our freedom – that freedom on which you and I were nourished and the very name of which has been sacred to us ever since our childhood.'

It was a long time since they had last met; but to their joy they found that in almost all questions they were of a single mind. Horn said nothing about already having made a like-minded acquaintance, to whom he was becoming ever more closely attached. There was so much else to talk about. But before they parted company he invited his friend out to dinner at Huvudsta the following Sunday.

During these days fierce struggles were raging in all the country towns of Sweden for the mandates of the Third Estate. In most places the king's partisans were victorious; but in Stockholm the outcome was different. Two days after the meeting between Horn and Ribbing, the elections took place. Businessmen and craftsmen alike, annoyed that the *riksdag* was not to be held in the capital, managed to get one oppositionist after another elected. Should anything happen, therefore, Pechlin and his associates were confident of the citizens' support. But they needed money; and the leading patriots enthusiastically began to gather a fund to be placed at the general's disposal.

The conflict grew more acute. Orders began to arrive as to which troops were to be ordered to the scene of the *riksdag*. Three hundred men of the First Life Guards and two hundred of the Second, together with fifty Light Dragoons, were to march to Gävle, where two hundred soldiers from the Hälsingland Regiment were already stationed. Seven hundred and fifty men – not to mention great numbers of police – just to do guard duty! This seemed a terrifyingly large force. But public anxiety grew still further when it was realized how meticulously both officers and rank and file were being selected. Only officers whose youth or political innocence inspired confidence in the authorities were being chosen.

On Sunday, 15 January, some friends of Count and Countess Horn came driving out in their covered sledges through Solna Wood to Huvudsta Manor. Near the shores of Lake Ulfsunda the little old timber house lay deep in snow. Claes Horn was a superb host. His very appearance captured all the ladies' hearts. Tall and slender, with an aristocratic nose, he had large dreamy eyes and a mouth quick to smile. Another of his charms was his ability to write verses almost on a par with those of his distinguished friends in the Utile Dulci Society: the witty poet and incisive critic Kellgren, and the dreamy

Oxenstierna. And how he could play! On both flute and violin he was a virtuoso. With equal virtuosity he could discuss the art of fortifications, redoubts and bastions with his fellow-officers in the fortification office. To Horn, such problems were mere child's play. Three years ago, however, he had broken off a promising military career in protest against his father's outrageous imprisonment. The day after the aged General Horn had been arrested at the previous *riksdag*, Claes Horn had gone straight to the king and demanded audience. Being refused, he had demanded to be admitted to the same prison as his father. This too had been refused, as were his demands to be allowed to visit him. As soon as he had got home that evening he had penned his letter of resignation.

Now dinner was over. The fare, as usual, had been delicious; but under all the gaiety smouldered Horn's and his guests' political anxieties. Live ammunition, it was reported, was being issued to those guards units which, in a couple of days' time, were to leave for Gävle. That sounded ominous. In one of the small rooms the host chanced to find himself alone with Ribbing and Anckarström, who was also one of the guests, and they turned to discussing what counter-measures the patriots should resort to. As they discussed the matter the two counts became extremely agitated:

'Unless we can get rid of Gustaf III nothing will be any good,' Anckarström interposed. Ribbing shrugged.

'And when that will be God alone knows. Horn and I cannot imagine ourselves doing anything.'

'If I had the chance, I'd do it.'

'He's a devil of a fellow, you know,' Horn joked, pointing at Anckarström. Ribbing did not reply.

'Where could one get a chance to do it?' Anckarström persisted. Obviously, he had only a single thought in his head.

'At some public spectacle, I suppose, or out at Haga,' Horn opined.

'At Haga there are guards; many, it's said. Looks difficult.

At the Opera, I don't know. Supposing we could take the box next to the king's?'

'That's always taken by the diplomatic corps,' objected Ribbing.

'Mightn't it be possible when the king's going from his big box to the little one?'

'It might.'

At that moment Countess Horn came in, wondering where her husband had got to, and their conversation was interrupted. But the three men agreed to meet again the following day at Anckarström's place.

This was not the first time Ribbing had met Anckarström. Ten years earlier they had got to know each other cursorily while both were serving in the Guards. But this was a meeting in quite different circumstances, a meeting of whose consequences they had as yet not the faintest intimation. They differed greatly in birth and breeding; but one and the same thought inspired them both: that at all costs they must bring about a change. Neither Horn nor Ribbing, on the other hand, felt the same fanatical urge to act as obsessed that dismissed guards captain and – in his own opinion – innocent victim of injustice, Jakob Johan Anckarström.

Next day both counts came to the humdrum room overlooking the yard. Anckarström showed them his weapons.

'These pistols of mine are no good,' he said, disgruntled. 'If only I could buy some better ones.'

'I've a couple of good pistols you can borrow,' said Horn. They resumed yesterday's interrupted topic.

'If we could get hold of a box in the second circle,' Anckarström said, 'we could go there, and as the king goes from one of his boxes to the other I could seize my opportunity. I could shoot him in the passage.'

Anckarström felt the two counts were hardly of the right mettle and that they were only agreeing with him for appearances' sake. But at least it was a plan, and as such worth trying. As Horn was anyway going down into town, Anckarström asked him to inquire about a box. Afterwards, in the afternoon, they could meet again at the Misses Linnerhjelm's.

The two counts were not as hesitant as Anckarström had supposed. They knew exactly which box it was they should try to borrow – the third or fourth from the king's. Closer than that it would hardly be possible to get. That winter the box had been let to the young Countess Lovisa Hierta. She had just deserted her husband and children, and was hoping for a swift divorce in order to remarry – and the man of her heart was none other than Adolf Ribbing. She, too, was an associate of the Huvudsta family. So she had nothing at all against lending her box to Claes Horn for the evening. And certainly – by all means – he was most welcome to bring a friend with him.

Anckarström was told the good news in the Misses Linnerhjelm's apartment. With a loaded pistol in his pocket, he followed Horn to the box at the Opera. On the programme that evening was *Thetis och Pelée*, an opera which the king himself had drafted twenty years earlier. Now as Gustaf III appeared in his great royal box at the back of the first circle he was greeted as usual with polite applause. Ribbing, walking about amid the standing audience in the pit, was confused by the suddenness of it all, and doubted very much whether Anckarström would dare to proceed from words to deeds. The performance began. All eyes turned to the stage, where mythological personages began singing Uttini's interminable voluptuous arias. Only Anckarström's gaze remained fixed upon the king. As soon as the king, obedient to his habit, got up to go to his little box with its grille – the *oeil de boeuf* near the stage, on the right hand side of the first circle – it was Anckarström's intention to slip out into the dark passage and there fire the murderous shot. But as one act followed another, the king did not once stir from where he was sitting.

'Perhaps it is God's will that he shall live? Perhaps God is holding His protecting hand over him?' thought Horn to himself, as Anckarström and he left the opera together.

To his disappointment Anckarström noticed that the count seemed relieved that nothing had happened, and they parted without fixing another meeting. After so many tense hours Anckarström felt rather tired, but not for a moment did he mean to change his plans. If only he felt more support from the two counts! But when words were to be turned into actions they always seemed to shrink back.

'This isn't good enough,' said Captain Anckarström to himself. 'I'll go to the theatre. Perhaps I can do it there.'

Next day was the day for the troops' departure. The drums beat. Echoing among the houses, they summoned the Blue and Yellow Life Guards from their billets to assembly points on Norrmalmstorg – the great square outside the Opera – and at the Haymarket. The soldiers did not grumble at being called to the colours nor at the prospect of a long march across the snow-covered plains, northwards to Gävle. Even though it was only to do guard duty – God be thanked – they had been told they were to get the same pay as on active service.

Noblemen looking out of their windows on Drottninggatan saw them march away in swirling snow towards the northern customs barrier, and wondered what their errand really was. Were the king's proposals going to be so tough he could not hope to push them through without resorting to force? Or were all these troop movements merely evidence of his fear of the opposition?

That evening Anckarström, alone, went to the play, to see what possibilities the old Bollhus Theatre might offer. Here, just opposite the Palace, the French troupe gave performances on Wednesdays and Fridays, while on Tuesdays and Saturdays the actors from the king's newly-formed Royal Dramatic Theatre used the house. Today was Tuesday. The tragedy *Olympie* was being sung to some newly-composed music. The king's box had been altered, and there were few people in the audience. That same day the newspapers had advertised boxes still to be rented for the first quarter of the year. It did not take Anckarström long to come to the conclusion that nothing could be done here.

But these difficulties in finding the right place to do his deed did not dishearten him. Rather, they spurred him to fresh reconnaissances. Two days later a masquerade ball was held at the Opera, and once again, with loaded pistols, he mingled with the crowd. But he made no attempt on the king's life this time either. Nor did Ribbing go with him. He had plenty of other things to see to before leaving next morning for the *riksdag*.

Just how serious his attempts were, Anckarström himself seems hardly to have realized. From Ribbing, incessantly coming and going in Pechlin's house, he knew that the plans were slowly maturing for a revolution. But Anckarström had no desire to know who else was involved in these conspiracies. The deed which alone would make such a change possible absorbed him entirely. He had been called to liberate his fatherland from the tyrant, he felt; and he seems to have believed that once the bloody deed was done, all other problems would solve themselves of their own accord. But Pechlin wasn't so sure. From many points of view – with the royalist troops marching away across the snowy plains of Uppland, and their more rebelliously disposed officers forced to remain behind in the capital – the time was ripe. As for the support of the middle-class Stockholmers, hadn't the recent elections clearly shown they were to be counted on? At Gävle things would be more difficult. But Pechlin contented himself with Anckarström's reconnaissances, and bided his time.

One of the general's closest henchmen was a lieutenant-colonel called Pontus Lilliehorn, who held the rank of major in the First Life Guards. A splendid figure of a man, worshipped by his soldiers, Lilliehorn, who had grown up at court, owed more to the king than most noblemen of his generation. He had fought bravely in the war against Russia and during a skirmish with the Muscovites his unit had captured a cannon, a deed which had been honoured by the cannon being placed outside the guard wing, in the outer courtyard of the Palace. Yet the war had been illegally started – under the terms of his own constitution the king had had no right to declare war – and it was this war, wasting so many lives and so much money, which had raised doubts in Lilliehorn's mind as to the wisdom with which his country was being governed. If all this feckless waste, this tyranny, were allowed to go on, Sweden would soon be ruined.

Pechlin was a student of human nature. When the moment came, Lilliehorn's untarnished reputation, he realized, and the universal respect enjoyed by that officer, would be great moral assets. Pechlin himself was going to attend the Gävle *riksdag*, and if anything happened there Lilliehorn was to be the man responsible for maintaining order in the capital. Those words were often on the conspirators' lips: maintain order in the capital. A cautious expression – which could upset no one.

In the general's circle were others equally devoted to the cause. Not such fanatics, of course, as those hotheads Horn and Ribbing. But older and more experienced. For instance, there was Baron Thure Stensson Bielke. Despite poor health and a twisted body, Bielke, who had little taste for urban occupations, had tried his hand at farming. But his farming had been unprofitable and as the debts of his Södermanland estate at Eklöv grew and grew, he consoled himself by playing the clavichord and burying himself in the treasures of Greek and Latin literature. Bielke did not like the king. He went daily in terror lest the monarch, by some sudden or drastic action, should strip the nobility of estates and privileges alike.

This was an issue which could always be counted on to rouse Bielke from his lethargy and transform him into an audacious and excitable talker. Pechlin, for his part, was somewhat critical of Bielke. A muddle-headed chatterbox, he thought him, who did not always stick to the truth. But Bielke had many good middle-class connections in Stockholm, and these, Pechlin supposed, could always come in handy when the moment for action arrived. As for Bielke, he was dreaming of a lucrative post in the new government. He was counting on the revolution to restore his fortunes. Who knew? Perhaps he might even be called on to take charge of the nation's finances? These were currently in the hands of the king's minister, Håkansson. Son of a peasant, Håkansson's father had been speaker of the Fourth Estate during the Age of Freedom.

If Bielke was a man of doubtful capacity, Pechlin listened with so much the greater respect to what the two brothers von Engeström had to say. Jakob, the older of these, was a deeply religious and conscientious civil servant. During the last phase of the Age of Freedom he had begun a promising career, but after Gustaf III's seizure of power in 1772 the monarch's way of favouring courtiers and military men, regardless of whether they had any talent or not, had robbed Jakob von Engeström of promotion. As the years had gone by, frustrated ambition had made him increasingly critical of the régime. What had made him most indignant of all and convinced him – as it had so many others – that a change must be effected in the nation's affairs, was the king's wilful interferences in the constitutional rights of the Estates. Jakob von Engeström had even drafted a new constitution, to come into force after the revolution.

The second of the von Engeström brothers was Johan. He, too, felt his career had been nipped in the bud by the king's 1772 *coup d'état*, and it had not been long before he had become one of his most rancorous opponents. An enthusiast for theories of natural law, he was always ready to oppose the royal despotism. He had also been one of the men arrested at the last *riksdag*, and was an often-seen guest at the house of General Pechlin, who shared his views.

That week members of the *riksdag* were making their way to Gävle from every corner of Sweden. It was a week of severe cold. Nor did their journey grow less troublesome as they neared their goal. At Älvkarleby, the last posting stage for those coming from the south, Saturday, 21 January, was a day of crowding and confusion. A blizzard was blowing, and along the way the snow was so deep it covered the tips of the fences and in the villages reached up to the peasants' roof-trusses. With the snow whirling all about them, the nation's representatives were obliged to wait for hours for post horses. At Harnäs, just outside Gävle, they were halted once more, this time by a piquet of the Hälsingland Regiment, whose soldiers ran out with lowered bayonets:

'Halt! Show your passport!'

Everyone had his passport taken from him into the guardhouse, examined, countersigned and after a while – during which the soldiers stood pointing their bayonets at him – returned. But only those who could legitimize themselves as members of the *riksdag* were allowed to pass. All others were brusquely turned back. Those who came from the north and west met with the same treatment as soon as they reached a guardhouse. Quartered in the villages all about, the troops which had been sent to Gävle formed a ring around the town. Ministers of foreign powers, who had come to see with their own eyes what was going on, reported to their governments that, more than anything else, Gävle resembled a blockaded city.

The aristocrats knew very well that if the king intended to use force, it would chiefly be against themselves. On leaving home, therefore, they had taken care to arm themselves with military or pocket pistols, and taken such fond farewells of their loved ones that they might have been going to the wars.

This was why Anders David Kauffman, a Stockholm pistol-maker whose shop stood in Västra Bangränd Alley, hard by the Haymarket, had found nothing surprising about the visit paid to him some time in the middle of the month by Captain Anckarström. Anckarström had wanted a couple of demi-pistols to be repaired for him before leaving for Gävle. The apprentice who accepted the order had promised to see to it that the locks should not misfire. On this point the captain was adamant. Unfortunately, at that moment the stock-maker had died, so when Anckarström, on the eve of setting out for Gävle, had come back to fetch his pistols, they had not been ready for him – nor, indeed, was he to get them back until he came back from the *riksdag*. And with that Anckarström had to be content. Once again he stipulated that the locks must not misfire.

III

THE POWER GAME AT THE GÄVLE RIKSDAG

When Gustaf III left Stockholm, the Crown Prince was sitting beside him in the covered sledge. As usual, the king was travelling at a furious gallop, with an escort of two horsemen ahead of the sledge and six after it. In order not to trouble the peasantry along the main road to provide him with horses, he took other roads northwards and spent the night with his governor, af Nordin, at Forsbacka Ironworks.

On Sunday evening, 22 January, the king made his ceremonial entry into Gävle. Now he was not in his sledge, but in his great state coach. With all the difficulty in the world it had been dragged through a hundred miles of snowdrifts from the capital. On either side walked guards and torch-bearers, and at the town customs barrier the archbishop, the governor of the province and the mayor and council of the town all stood bowing.

'Long live the king, father of the peasantry!' shouted a group of peasants.

But sceptical patriots were quick to note that most of the shouting was being done by a type of people whose services had never before been found necessary in Gävle; namely policemen. And when, later in the evening, the representatives of the nation snuggled down under silk eiderdown or more substantial sheepskin, they were awakened out of their slumbers from time to time by the tramp of marching patrols. Such, for a whole month to come, was to be their music.

The *riksdag* was to begin its sessions on the morrow. In the morning the king, who was occupying both floors of the governor's residence, gave a *levée* in his bedchamber. It had been furnished much like his great State Bedchamber in the Palace at Stockholm, with a bannister round the bed. In the crush Gustaf was astonished to see many of the noblemen whom he had arrested at the last *riksdag*. On both sides the art of dissimulation celebrated triumphs. All were received by him in the friendliest fashion. But every glance, each word – or lack of a word – was critically and silently interpreted by those standing around. And when the king failed – was it intentionally, or by mere oversight? – to greet Count Magnus Brahe, it caused a sensation.

The tension was growing. The king was moved; only with difficulty could he keep up appearances. There was an embarrassed silence. Anxiously, Elis Schröderheim, the corpulent Secretary of State who was in charge of the proceedings, noted signs of a royal *inquiètude*. The right side of Gustaf's jaw sagged, he had a nervous way of throwing his cape over his shoulders and adjusting his lace neckerchief. Again and again he turned sharply on his heel. Schröderheim intervened. With a ceremonious bow he announced that the heralds were waiting to receive from the hand of His Majesty the proclamation with which, to fanfares and drumrolls, they were to ride about the town and announce the *riksdag*'s opening. Immediately everything was again under control. After the ceremony with the heralds, the king handed the staff of office of the First Estate to his former minister of finance, Baron Erik Ruuth. Still undischarged of responsibility for his stewardship, Ruuth could not be suspected of any partiality towards the opposition.

In the hastily erected Hall of State the *riksdag* opened with all pomp and circumstance. The monarch took his seat on his throne, and on stools in front of him sat the Lord Chancellor Wachtmeister and the Lord Chamberlain, that gifted poet, John Gabriel Oxenstierna. At the previous *riksdag* the Council had been summarily abolished; so the purple mantles of the councillors, all of them high aristocrats, which normally would have added brilliance to the scene about the throne, were conspicuous by their absence. To the nobles this was but one more unpleasant reminder of their own overthrow. But they gave no sign of their dissatisfaction. Pechlin and the men around him had agreed to avoid any overt struggle for power at Gävle. They intended to wait and see what the other Estates would have to say. Such compliant behaviour would give the king no pretext for the sort of violence to which he had resorted at the last *riksdag*. Immediately on his arrival the previous evening the king had held a *cour*. And to show their compliant attitude some of the patriots had presented themselves at the castle. It had been for the same reason that their leaders, Brahe, De Geer and Stierneld – all of whom had been at Pechlin's dinner – had attended the royal *levée*. But if the peace was to be kept, then the king for his part must not provoke the First Estate by making impossible demands. Was the hateful Act of Union and Security, for instance, going to be read out in the Hall of State? If so, it would be tantamount to a declaration of war. The Act had given the king the right to appoint such advisers – insofar as he felt he needed any – as he saw fit, whether nobles or commoners. Thus the wheel of history had come full cycle, and the age-old institution of the Council, which in the previous reign had been omnipotent and had succeeded in reducing the crown to a mere symbol, was itself now reduced to nothing. The Act also gave the monarch complete freedom to appoint and dismiss civil servants, thus crushing the power of the bureaucracy, which had hitherto been largely recruited from among the ranks of the nobility, and given capable commoners a better chance of reaching the top. Rather than recognize this Act of Security the nobility were ready to sacrifice their lives to the last man.

All of which had been made plain to the Earl Marshal. He had warned the king of the prevailing mood: but Gustaf III had assured Brahe and his fellow-nobles that no mention would be made of the Act of Security. This optimistic promise had so pacified the opposition that even those on the government side were pleasantly surprised by the nobles' conciliatory attitude. But when rumour of all this reached Stockholm, Johan von Engeström wrote back to his brother Jackob, at Gävle:

'I have heard that His Majesty is most polite to the nobility, and the nobility *vice versa*. I hope, however, our friends will not be duped by the serpent's cunning.'

The reason why the Estates had been summoned was to remedy the distraught finances of the kingdom. This was the all-overshadowing problem, and it could not be put off a day longer. The honest burghers of Gävle must therefore have opened their eyes very wide indeed when they saw all the luxury in which the representatives both of the nobility and of the commons were indulging. Not only up at the castle was the table laid for numerous courtiers and their guests. Earl Marshal Ruuth, too, had laid his for thirty persons and from time to time gave balls. Governor af Nordin's was laid for twenty guests. The archbishop's for sixteen – there were only fifty-two representatives of the clergy. Ahlman, the Vice-Governor of Stockholm, who was secretary to the Peasants, had had his table laid for thirty. In a word, the crown was footing the bill with such lavishness that every day almost two hundred ravenous members of the Swedish parliament were being entertained to dinner at the public expense. Nowhere was the luxury greater, however, than in the lodgings of the royal favourite, Major-General Gustaf Mauritz Armfelt, Chancellor of Abo University, Knight of the Order of the Seraphim, and one of the 'Eighteen Immortals' of Gustaf's newly founded Academy. Before his door stood posted sentries from a guard of honour, a unique distinction. Each day some thirty guests dined at his table, while eight German musicians, clad in silver-braided livery, provided a *taffelmusik*. In order that his fare should out-vie all others', Armfelt had borrowed Princess Sofia Albertina's *maître d'hôtel*, regarded as the ablest in Sweden, and, assuming the airs of a prince of the blood, arranged for himself to be served before all others. Armfelt's cutlery was of silver-gilt, and beside his place at table stood a salt-cellar of solid gold.

Each time Armfelt had to go up to the castle he was carried by two liveried lackeys in a sedan chair and the chair was followed by a bodyguard of stalwart uniformed clerks from a business house. His severe wound, sustained in the war against Russia, made it difficult for him to walk, he claimed. His cherubic person, framed in so much magnificence, was further enhanced by a swarm of servants. Such extravagance displeased the Estates. To some extent it even displeased the king.

Several restaurateurs had come from Stockholm. They were to be responsible for all food and drink in the clubs set up for the various Estates.

Within the city barriers, nobles, clergy and burghers were free to come and go as they pleased. For the peasantry things were not quite so easy. The secretary for their Estate, Per Zackarias Ahlman, kept a sharp eye on them, a duty he had performed at the last *riksdag*, too, with unusual thoroughness. Now, as the Fourth Estate assembled for the first time in a classroom of the tumbledown and unbearably draughty grammar school, Ahlman addressed the wretched freezing peasants in schoolmasterly fashion, fulsomely welcoming them as sincere friends and honest farmers. At the last *riksdag*, he said, the peasants had acquired rights and privileges which they had long coveted in vain – a reference to the extension of their rights to purchase land. At that time, he said, the foundations had been laid of the prosperity of the country-folk and for its continuance for the future.

'But,' he went on, threateningly, 'if you should let yourselves be deluded, if you should be seduced into seeking counsel and protection elsewhere than from the king, or deviate from that path into which you have entered, then you may rest assured of the fall and ruin of the peasantry.'

The 'insidious seducers' were to be found, of course, in the other Estates. So, to make quite sure that no political fraternization took place, all the 160 peasants had been quartered together in one particular street on the far side of the town. Sentries from the garrison guarded the area, and police prevented all visits from outsiders. Whenever they went to their club the peasants had to go in a flock, accompanied by a policeman or a royal lackey in livery.

This was unpleasant. But it was outweighed by the delights there awaiting them. They were invited to eat and drink free, gratis and for nothing; wine and brandy flowed in rivers – and the crown footed the bill. Afterwards, conducted to their assembly hall in the grammar school, they were all so helplessly drunk that they acquiesced feebly in whatever measures were proposed to them. Ahlman held them completely in his grip.

The Clergy and the Burghers, too, danced meekly to the king's pipe. Only in the First Estate – to which the Hospital or Lesser Church had been allotted as a place of assembly – were the opposition in an overwhelming majority. And this was why noblemen were sometimes treated more openly with suspicion, as they went about the town, than they were at the castle. One nobleman of no particular importance, visiting the Burgher's club, was brusquely turned away by the hot-tempered Stockholm brewer, Abraham Westman. Westman took the opportunity to let this gentleman know what he thought about the aristocracy. The news reached Armfelt's ears, and that evening he gave a sinister account of the intermezzo in the castle drawing-room, saying there was nothing he would more enjoy than to fling himself with fixed bayonets on the thousand devils in the House of Nobles. This fear, that the aristocrats might start some nasty business, spread to the peaceable citizens of Gävle. And one evening Ribbing, walking lighted candle in hand across the dark yard of his house, heard his host shout out at him that he was one of those so-and-so's who had come to set fire to the town. Ribbing blew out his light. And next day moved to other lodgings.

According to Gustaf III's plan, the real work of the *riksdag* was to be done by the Secret Commission. This commission was to hold its meetings under his own chairmanship, on the ground floor of the castle. One of the first things to be done, therefore, was to choose electors, who in turn should elect the commission. From the results of these elections it would instantly transpire whether royalists or patriots were in a majority. Among the peasants the outcome was certain; Ahlman made sure they would elect only persons pleasing to the king. In the two other lower Estates the result was the same. Only in the Nobles were the patriots, despite the king's attempts to influence the election, in a big majority. Among the electors were Brahe, Charles De Geer, Bogislaus Staël von Holstein and Stierneld – those same influential gentlemen who had taken part in Pechlin's dinner, at which the plan of campaign for the coming *riksdag* had first been drawn up.

The political structure of the secret commission was the same: a large royalist majority in the three lower Estates, and among the noblemen nothing but patriots. This was exactly the same state of affairs as at the last *riksdag*, and now everyone was wondering anxiously whether it would not again lead to hard blows. Certainly there was a risk of it. The nobility seemed to have intentionally elected men who were all thoroughly negative towards the king. One was Jakob von Engeström. Another was Brahe's brother-in-law, Claes Lewenhaupt; the king detested him, and at one of the commission's sessions cut him dead.

The king led the negotiations with a firm hand. At the opening of the *riksdag* he had reminded its members of the occasion three years before, when, with the war at its crisis, he had appealed to the Estate for their support:

'I knew how turbulent people's feelings were. I knew how far I could go. But I was relying on the nation's generosity. Nor was I deceived. I gathered you together. Our deliberations were troubled, but the realm needed speedy help. You gave it. The army showed its Swedish mettle, showed itself not unworthy of its forefathers, it fought bravely. Finland was saved and peace restored. Such has been the course of events.'

But now the financial situation had to be presented to the secret commission, and such high-sounding phrases were out of place. The war had cost twenty-three million gold *riksdaler*. The last *riksdag* had only allocated ten. So there was a debt of thirteen million. How was this to be paid? This was one of the questions the king wished the commission to discuss. But he also desired its opinion concerning the double currency; the par-value banknotes, and the national-debt credit notes. More than eight million of the latter were currently in circulation, and it was not easy to see how this sum could be reduced within the forseeable future.

More conveniently to look into these matters, the secret commission appointed two sub-committees, one of which was to examine the administration of the national debt. At the meeting at which these two sub-committees were elected, the Lord Chancellor Wachtmeister was present. This was all that was needed for the noblemen, with the painful events of the last *riksdag* fresh in their memory, to fear for their personal security. Were they going to be arrested this time, too? To all questions the king replied with soothing answers.

Meanwhile all the other representatives who did not belong to the commission sat in their clubs and talked politics. Their excited conversations revolved more and more around the question of how things were to be arranged as between the old and new currencies. In the middle of the month the poet, Thomas Thorild, threw a firebrand. 'All Things Needful to the Realm's Finances', the self-assured poet entitled his pamphlet. In it he defended the current rate of exchange, and concluded with a few parting kicks at governments which involved their countries in wars and acted as if might were right. At Gävle the pamphlet was read and passionately discussed. Some laughed at Thorild's wild ideas; others thought they found pearls among them.

But the government acted. A decree forbade all printers to publish anything touching such matters as were being discussed by the Estates, and more especially financial issues. The representatives should stick to the dry facts offered them in the special *riksdag* newspaper. Published at the government's expense, *Historical and Political News* permitted no heresies. Notwithstanding the decree, another very sharp pen, inspired at top level, gave Thorild his answer. It too was written by a poet, Leopold, the king's intimate collaborator in his plays and operas. Leopold did not mince his words. Even in his introduction he ridiculed his opponent with anal epithets. His piece of writing was called: 'Letter to the great and remarkable author TH.... who, after legislating in the realm of letters, has done his business in the finances'.

In the first Estate Pechlin never spoke. There the opposition's views were presented by Jakob von Engeström, Bielke and Ribbing. For his part the general sat in his lodgings, sucking his pipe. But every evening until late into the night a stream of visitors brought him the latest news, discussed matters, and got their marching orders. Sometimes as many as twenty or thirty people would be assembled in his cramped rented rooms. Usually Ribbing was there; almost as often Bielke, and Jakob von Engeström. Sometimes the league's most enthusiastic adjutant, Major Bogislaus Staël von Holstein; and once or twice Magnus Brahe. On two occasions Anckarström's sharp features were to be glimpsed in the wintry dusk.

One day, when Pechlin's rooms were packed with people, a royal messenger suddenly appeared and invited him to be among those who were to carry the king's baldachin in a procession. The old man turned the invitation down flat:

'I'm hardly strong enough to carry myself,' he snapped.

As soon as the royal messenger's tall waving plume had disappeared through the door, the housekeeper, Maja Lisa

Lidberg, received a reprimand for having let the fellow in.

Maja Lisa paid no attention to what the gentlemen were discussing. But young Mamsell Regina Pettersson did. Mamsell Regina ran Pechlin's household – he was a widower – and acted as hostess when he entertained. As Maja Lisa came with a tray of glasses and bottles she saw Mamsell Regina eavesdropping outside the door; almost before she had time to put down her tray, she received a sign to make herself scarce.

Mamsell Regina was a girl who had her wits about her. One morning the general already had a lot of visitors; in the ante-room a hairdresser was doing Mamsell Regina's hair. Suspecting this hairdresser of being one of Ahlman's spies she called Pechlin's page, Nisse Åberg, and told him to jump up and down and make so much noise that the supposed spy would not be able to catch a word of what was being said within.

In communicating with their allies in Stockholm the conspirators had to take every precaution against their letters falling into Liljensparre's hands. The Chief of Police had no qualms about slitting open letters and then crudely sticking them down again, forwarding them to their addressees. Code names had to be used. Pechlin was called 'the Inspector'. Lilliehorn, now the opposition's supreme commander in the capital, went under the name of 'Neptune'. Even the political forces struggling for supremacy could not be called by their right names. Baron Carl Göran Bonde belonged to the intimate circle of freemasons around Duke Charles, the king's brother; without openly revealing his adherence to the opposition, Bonde, too, was critical of the king. In a letter to his good friend Baron Gustaf Adolf Reuterholm, then living in Italy, he sent a report on the political situation in the first phase of the *riksdag*:

Ida is growing bigger every day, but here and there the Tartar is beginning to smoke in the ashes. I know with some certainty that a

Parnassus is silently ripening and that its tutelary deity has no high titles. He bases himself on Lethe. But when?

Doubtless the Chief of Police, had he opened that letter, would have been no little confounded. But Reuterholm, who had the key of the cipher, knew that Ida meant 'despotism', the Tartar 'freedom', Parnassus 'revolution' and Lethe – 'death'. So Reuterholm, the man who a year or so later was to be the virtual dictator of Sweden, was not kept in ignorance of the plans which were afoot.

Invisible ink had to be used, and all letters were inserted for safety into books sent by reliable couriers between Gävle and Stockholm. Ribbing's cousin and room-mate Kurck was one such courier. Another was Lieutenant Ture Funck.

Anckarström had brought a pair of pocket pistols and a pair of large pistols with him to Gävle. He saw the king taking his incognito walks after the meetings of the commission. It would not have been impossible for Anckarström to get close enough to fire a shot. But after talking the matter over with Ribbing when they met in the nobles' club or at Ribbing's lodgings, he had been informed by Ribbing, who in his turn was taking advice from Pechlin, that, before giving the signal for action, the general wanted to wait and see what dice the king would throw.

Two quiet weeks passed. Then the two sub-committees, having completed their investigations, presented them to the secret commission.

On 16 February the commission voted on the financial sub-committee's proposals. These were accepted by the Clergy, the Burghers and the Peasants. Only the representatives of the Nobility rejected them out of hand. They were flatly against any regulation of the rate of exchange as between the two currencies. Jakob von Engeström uttered a warning against the inflation which he said must follow if the number of banknotes was increased in order to liquidate the costs of the war. But all this aristocratic resistance went for nothing. Two days later the secret commission approved the excerpts from the minutes to be presented to the Estates. Therewith the secret commission had done its real business, and everyone could count on a breathing space before the debates in the various Estates began.

But then, suddenly, the king had one of his whims. The monotony of social life at Gävle, that dull little north Swedish town, was boring him to death. He was longing for a change. On 21 February, Shrove Tuesday, a masked ball was to be held at the Opera. Masquerades were one of Gustaf's favourite diversions. And he intended to go up to Stockholm for it. Besides, so light-hearted an excursion from the centre of political events would serve to show how calmly and expertly matters were being handled. It would impress the opposition, and stir the admiration of Europe.

But the court was deeply disturbed at the idea. Already, in Stockholm, the rooms in the Palace were being heated and lit. The bodyguards were under orders to receive the king, whose arrival might be expected at any time. At Gävle the courtiers had all the trouble in the world to get him to give up his whim. In the end they succeeded. But with depressing effects on the king's mood.

The Estates were to meet on 20 February. The most burning question, more likely than any other to cause a general conflagration, was the rate of exchange: i.e., between the bank notes, which were based on gold, and the credit notes, which possessed only their paper value. According to the secret commission's proposal, launched by Minister of Finance Håkansson, there should be a fixed rate. When people paid their debts, all interest in excess of four per cent should be payable in credit notes. So should the capital sum, but in that case with a fixed supplement of six per cent.

The general outline of these proposals had leaked out and at a Sunday dinner at the Lord Chancellor's big house on the market place, attended by persons from all parties, a violent altercation had broken out between one of Håkansson's supporters and Knut Kurck. Kurck, who belonged heart and soul to the opposition, had made some reference to Thorild's pamphlet on the country's finances.

Elsewhere in the town, that February Sunday was even more rowdily celebrated. Any resistance in the Peasant Estate had to be stifled in its infancy; so the peasants' representatives were invited to a stupendous bean-feast at their club. All night the drunken orgy went on. No one was allowed to go back to his lodgings – perhaps no one wanted to. And when at last the February sun rose over the frozen Baltic, its pale light shone down on a flock of peasants, boisterous and livid of face, staggering in a state of advanced hangover to their class-room, there to reach their wise decisions. Meanwhile all the windows of their club-room had been thrown wide open, and a foul stench, not only of beer and brandy, but also of vomit, floated out into the town. From the windows down to the snowy ground the outside walls were bespattered with frozen cascades of vomit, 'as on the sides of a ship laden with seasick passengers in a raging sea' – but infinitely more plentiful. The cold being unusually intense and persistent, these traces of their feast could not be removed, but were 'long the cynosure of all the Estates of the Realm and all the inhabitants of Gävle'.

Meanwhile the peasants were trying to make up their minds about the secret commission's proposals. In view of their gravity, one tenant farmer from Stockholm County demanded an adjournment. But the others, exhausted and drunk as lords, shouted out that the proposals be instantly adopted. And that was that. The Clergy reached the same unanimous decision; also the Burghers. Only the Nobles insisted on a thorough debate before voting. The 20 February was the anniversary of the hateful arrests at the last *riksdag* in 1789, so they were particularly loath to appear compliant. Until now the Secretary of State, Elis Schröderheim, who had been keeping the minutes of the secret commission, had not had a moment to himself. But this day he devoted to a visit to the Hospital Church, to see how Ruuth was doing his job as Earl Marshal. Schröderheim had been sitting there no more than an hour when an urgent message from the king summoned him up to the castle.

It was midday; but the cold was so severe that the king had not felt like getting out of bed, where he still lay, turning the pages of a duty journal of the Stockholm National Guard. Good reports had been coming in from the Estates, so the king was in a sunny humour.

'Now, my dear Schröderheim, we must bring this *riksdag* to a close.'

Ringing for a gentleman of the chamber, Gustaf gave orders for a state coach to be brought round from the coach house straight away, with three lackeys.

'It is my wish,' he said, 'that you go at once to the Estates and invite them to the Crown Prince's examination this afternoon at five o'clock.'

Schröderheim was astounded. Raised a thousand objections. The wretched Crown Prince and his tutor, he expostulated, ought not to be subjected to such a thing! And how could the Estates have time to elect deputies at such short notice? Or these deputies have time to dress? It was all of no avail. Schröderheim, in the state coach, was packed off down to the market place, where flocks of representatives were either strolling about or else going off home to their dinners. Mr Speaker was equally surprised, but promised to send some deputies. Most upset of all was the Lord Chancellor. The nobles, he saw, would suspect all this haste and hurry as being a device by the king to forestall their attendance. So heavy with suspicion was the atmosphere.

Everything was arranged, however; and on the stroke of five the examination began. All were impressed by the Crown Prince's judicious answers. But after it was over, just as the king was about to hold his *grand couvert*, a most painful contretemps occurred. All the nobles, with their Earl Marshal at their head, walked out of the castle. Not one stayed to dinner. Was it not 20 February – of all days in the calendar the most hateful to the nobles and aristocrats of Sweden?

This demonstration of overt hostility threw the king into a fury. The least he had hoped for had been a gesture of politeness towards the Crown Prince. But there was no explaining it away. And the *riksdag*, which up to now had gone off calmly enough, suddenly assumed quite another character. The truce was over – as could be seen next day, when the Nobles began to debate the secret commission's proposals. Thure Stensson Bielke violently criticized the king's measures. The memorandum, he said, confirmed his notion that warlike enterprises were ill-suited to nations with such empty treasuries. And if, even so, he was going to vote for the commission's proposal, it was, he said, only because he regarded the mutual harmony of the Estates as basic to the happiness of society. Bielke himself, as we have seen, was heavily laden with debts, mostly incurred in coin of the realm. The commission's proposal should therefore have been to his advantage, since it permitted debtors to repay part of their debts in credit notes. But this did not prevent Bielke, that obedient hanger-on of Pechlin and other wealthy capitalists, from criticizing it.

Ribbing, hot-tempered as usual, reprimanded the other Estates for reaching so hasty a decision in a matter of such great consequence. The Nobles, he insisted, should delay their decision for one day. Others agreed. Now verily the ghosts of the fateful 1789 *riksdag* were walking again! Was it not on this day three years ago that the Act of Union and Security had been forced through? The nobles threatened to go on talking until midnight if the Earl Marshal did not agree to an adjournment – only then would they suffer the motion to be passed, not a moment earlier! Earl Marshal Ruuth was in a quandary. The longer the debate went on, the stormier he feared it would become. So he gave way, and the question was adjourned. This action made the king even more furious, both with his Earl Marshal and with the Nobles.

Next day the debate was resumed, and in the end proposals were adopted in the First Estate, too. So, at last, the crucial question of the day had been settled.

But the noblemen's demonstrative walk-out after the Crown Prince's exam was more than the king could swallow. The *riksdag*, he now decided, should close in two days' time, on 24 February. Schröderheim was ordered to formulate its decisions and incorporate them in the speech of thanks for the Act of Security – which the commons were to address to the king – a step which the king had been advised to take by the two Nordin brothers, by Åhlman and by Håkansson. He himself was anxious to see the Act written into the constitution.

Schröderheim was terrified. To do this, he pointed out, would be to rescind the agreement made between the king and the Earl Marshal at the opening of the *riksdag*. No good could come of such a challenge. It would merely irritate the nobility still further, to no good purpose.

And indeed, the mere rumour of such a speech, thanking the king for the Act, was enough to throw the nobles into the gravest consternation. That evening a ball was held at the Earl Marshal's lodgings. When the dancing was at its height, a major, speaking on behalf of their host, suddenly called for silence. Something wholly unexpected, he announced, had occurred, such as necessitated an extra meeting of the entire First Estate. The dancing ended abruptly, and all the noblemen trooped off to the Hospital Church. It was one o'clock in the morning – but this was a case of *periculum in mora*. An insult had to be averted. After a long and wearisome discussion it was finally agreed that next morning, before the secret commission could meet, the Lord Chancellor Wachtmeister should try to induce the king to abstain from inserting the speech of thanks.

That night, in the circle of his friends, the Earl Marshal got no sleep. What would happen? Supposing the king insisted?

Or the Nobles were adamant? Might not the very thing happen which everyone feared before the *riksdag's* opening? And the king resort to force? Summoning a guards officer, the Earl Marshal asked him whether, in that event, the guards would intervene. The officer, speaking both on his own behalf and his men's, replied no, they wouldn't. The Earl Marshal gave a sigh of relief.

The following morning, more dead than alive, the eighteen aristocrats who were members of the secret commission presented themselves at the castle. Earl Marshal Ruuth was in despair. The Lord Chancellor furious. In the room where the secret commission was holding its sessions Count Adolf Hamilton, also furious, tired and fed up, stood glaring at the man who in his opinion was responsible for all this: Håkansson, the minister of finance. Suddenly an idea came into his head. Jokingly, he said to the Earl Marshal:

'Give Håkansson our regards and tell him we're going to assassinate him tomorrow morning at a quarter past eight.'

'An excellent idea,' replied Baron Ruuth.

Going up to Håkansson and taking him aside, Ruuth informed the wretched minister of finance, as a friend who had known him for a very long time, that he felt it his Christian duty to inform him that, things being as they were, the nobility had decided to kill both him and Ahlman tomorrow.

The trick worked. Taking the threat seriously, Håkansson went up to the king. And a few hours later Gustaf told his advisers he had abandoned his idea. The speech of thanks for the Act of Security would not be inserted in the *riksdag* minutes. The act, he said, was by now so well-established that to insert it in the speech would be superfluous. And with this decision the commons, when they presented themselves before the king, had to be content.

That day the question of the rate of exchange was again raised in the First Estate. For once Armfelt, hoping to enjoy the spectacle of the nobility at odds with itself, was present.

To Armfelt's astonishment no discussion took place at all. At their meeting in the early hours of the morning the nobles had already agreed to deny their enemies any such satisfaction. The bill had been read out, and Magnus Brahe had proposed that, seeing it had already been passed by the other three Estates, the nobility should simply let the matter rest there. The Nobles, that is, did not pass the bill regulating the rate of exchange; they simply registered their disapproval of it. Ribbing was appointed to lead the deputation which was to inform the commons.

The *riksdag* had scarcely lasted a month. The political temperature had been kept down to a point lower than anyone had dared hope, and only at the very end had it suddenly risen. But now Gustaf III was becoming more and more impatient to get back to his capital. There was a rumour of an impending mutiny in the Stockholm garrison, and even the commons were beginning to show signs of restiveness. The peasants had resisted a proposal that, in the event of the Crown Prince marrying before the next *riksdag*, a special tax should provide him with a wedding present. Had the *riksdag* lasted only a few more days, some thought, the peasants, notwithstanding all the government's lavish hospitality, might have sided against the king.

Ribbing was particularly well aware of this shifting of the wind. He urged an immediate revolution. And many agreed with him.

'It's no crime to murder a bad king,' declared Thure Stensson Bielke. Before his mind's eye floated such figures as Harmodios and Aristogeiton, Cassius and Brutus. Others said he was wrong. But he stuck to his views.

In the royalist camp Ribbing's activities in the First Estate and his haughty, defiant behaviour were causing anxiety. He was regarded as an extremist. So was his cousin Knut Kurck, who shared his lodgings both at Gävle and in Stockholm. And so were Gustaf Maclean and Claes Lewenhaupt. But Ribbing was the man they feared most. It was said that once, when the king had had his fortune told by the clairvoyant, Mamsell Arfwidsson, in her little room near St John's Chapel in Stockholm, she had warned him against the first man he should meet wearing a red waistcoat. Immediately afterwards the king had met Ribbing on the North Bridge. He had been wearing a red waistcoat.

But the hotheads yielded to Pechlin. What their blind fanaticism could not see, to the old intriguer was plain as a pikestaff. Even if Anckarström had shot the king during one of his incognito walks, it would have been by no means certain that the conspirators would have managed to seize power. What could they have done against seven hundred and fifty soldiers, all loyal to the government, and against the armed citizenry? Was it not achievement enough to have instilled such respect in the king and his supporters at the *riksdag*, that he had not dared lay hands on the bank's funds or write the Act of Security into the constitution? As for revolution, Pechlin had by no means dropped the idea. Ribbing had stirred up many passions. That, too, was good. Perhaps a better opportunity for direct action would present itself when they were all back in Stockholm.

IV

DAYS OF FAILURE

Friday, 24 February, when the brief *riksdag* was to close in the customary manner, was a day of horrible weather. The king desired nothing better than to get into his covered sledge and drive off home. But first, before he could do so, many things had to be attended to. One of the most delicate was the honours list. In the timber houses along the banks of the Gävle River, where the snow swirled and formed great drifts along the streets making the street doors difficult of access, obedient royalists were sitting by their morning stoves waiting for stars to fall from the throne and pin themselves on to their breasts.

At eight o'clock Elis Schröderheim, still without a moment to himself, was summoned to the royal bedchamber. From his *chaise percée* – or, in plain English, his commode – the king dictated to Schröderheim his speech to be given at the closing ceremony in the Hall of State. It was a hasty piece of work, and while the servants, with equal haste, were dressing the king, Schröderheim sat down in a little adjoining room to weed out all its French words. The speech, after all, was addressed not only to the nobility; less educated burghers and peasants had to be able to understand it, too. When the Secretary of State came back with his neatly pruned manuscript, the king, dressed, his hair curled and pomaded, was already standing there talking to General Taube. From his portfolio he took out the statutes of the Order of the Vasa, together with the decoration of a commander of that order. Weighing it thoughtfully in his hand he threw an inquiring glance at Schröderheim.

'No, I don't think so,' he said. And let it slip back into the portfolio.

For several days Gustaf had been suffering from a bad cold. Now, his cape flung over his shoulder, he went hurriedly down to the ground floor of the castle, where the secret commission was about to hold its last session. No matters of any importance remained to be dealt with. The two packets of the commission's minutes, neatly tied with silk ribbons, were to be ceremoniously sealed by the king and the speaker, and thereafter preserved in the State Archives and the offices of the House of Nobles. While this little ceremony was going on, the portly Schröderheim, at the king's behest, hurried upstairs again to fetch the statutes of the Order of the Vasa and the commander's decoration. Once again the king had changed his mind. As Schröderheim discreetly slipped them into his hand, Gustaf got up from his chair:

'Before closing these meetings,' he said, 'I wish to express my satisfaction at the spirit of unity and mutual confidence in which, despite the troublesome circumstances, they have been held throughout. How better express my satisfaction than by rewarding someone who has done us a real service? Among you, my good gentlemen of the nobility, I see a grey-headed man who at every *riksdag* for nearly half a century has distinguished himself and won the confidence of all. His insight and his habitual eloquent way of presenting his ideas have been of the greatest use. Your eyes turn already on Mr Frietzsky – it is to him I refer. I make him a commander of my Order of the Vasa, and it is my intention to knight him forthwith in your presence.'

All eyes turned to the back bench of the nobility, to where Claes Frietzsky was sitting. Frietzsky had once owned Storfors ironworks, in Värmland, had made a name for himself as an economist, and was certainly a veteran of the Swedish political scene. More than twenty years before, during the Age of Freedom, he had been a leader of the Cap Party. Later, in the eighties, like so many other citizens with a sense of responsibility in economics, he had joined the opposition and had become the closest ally of the former Hat leader, Count Fersen. The government had regarded Frietzsky as so dangerous that he had been one of the first to be arrested during the 1789 *riksdag*; also one of the last to be set at liberty. But during the *riksdag* now closing he had loyally placed his energy and knowledge at the disposition of the secret commission, and had played an active part in formulating the final plan for the country's finances. No one begrudged him a commander's decoration – and what a fine gesture of reconciliation on the monarch's part, towards one of his oldest and most dangerous opponents.

But the nobles present were seized with dismay. As they saw it this was but one more act of royal hypocrisy, and it infuriated them. For one moment they feared their hero might prove to have feet of clay. The commoners on the commission, too, were in an agony of apprehension, though for other reasons.

Claes Frietzsky got up and stepped forward. Raising his right hand, he bowed his head in homage.

'Forgive me, most gracious king,' he said, 'if I am so overcome by astonishment that I do not know how to express my gratitude. This honour which is offered to me, and which must always flatter any subject of the crown, flatters me the more for the manner in which Your Majesty does it to me. But the least temptation on my part to accept this decoration would render me unworthy of it.'

Whereupon Frietzsky told the company how, when the king had founded the Order of the Vasa at his coronation and had graciously informed the secret commission of this step, a lively discussion had broken out. He, Frietzsky, had been a member of the commission; and on his expressing his approval of the new honour, a clergyman had accused him of desiring it for himself. On which, he said, he had sworn an oath that, should the decoration ever be offered to him, he would not accept it.

'True, I went too far,' he concluded. 'But my oath stands,

and prevents me from accepting this honour from Your Majesty. Your Majesty, who cannot do otherwise than approve my sacrifice, must never doubt my gratitude.'

Frietzsky was justly admired for his eloquence. It had not failed him. Going up to the monarch, he twice kissed his hands.

'I beg Your Majesty, do not hold this against me!'

'My dear Frietzsky, your refusal is dictated by honour and virtue, and therefore is the easier for me to accept.'

The meeting was over. His cape flying, the king went back to his rooms. Downstairs the nobles crowded round their hero and patted him on the back.

With the weather so bad, the Estates were excused the customary procession to hear the sermon. From a profane building the Hall of State had in all haste been transformed into a sacred one. A pulpit, an altar, and a sacristy hung with ragged tapestries were all that was needed. While Bishop Olof Wallquist was officiating at the service, Schröderheim sat thinking irreverent thoughts; more than anything else, he reflected, these chattels reminded him of marionette tents. Hardly was the sermon over than the churchly decorations vanished in a flash and the Hall of State once again assumed its usual appearance.

The king went back to his bedroom; all Knights of the Seraphim and other beribboned gentlemen had been summoned to wait on him there. In their presence, af Nordin, the temporary provincial governor, and the minister of finance, Håkansson, together with some deserving members of the Burgher Estate, all received the Order of the Vasa. Next, the king was to receive deputations from the Estates. Schröderheim noticed something uneasy in the atmosphere; many people were standing staring out of the window, on tenterhooks until the Nobles' deputies should arrive with the Earl Marshal's staff of office. Salomon, the royal physician, brought the king his drops. And now here came the deputation, with Magnus Brahe at their head.

'Am I very pale?' the king inquired.

'Your Majesty shows signs of the day's fatigues,' Schröderheim replied with a happy turn of speech.

'Alas no. If only you knew how hard it is to be king.'

The deputation was admitted. After Brahe, with an elegant harangue, had handed back the marshal's staff, it was for the king to reply. His lower lip trembled. Tears came into his eyes:

'Count . . . count . . I accept from your hand . . . from your hand, count, I accept this staff of office. I had wished . . . I assure you that with all my royal grace and favour I remain devoted to the nobility . . . '

It was more than Gustaf could do to finish his speech. Impulsively, he embraced Brahe, the premier peer of the realm but also, to his grief, his chief enemy. Astonished, pale, eyes starting from his head, the count kissed the king's hand.

When the deputation had gone, the king said to Schröderheim:

'Ah ça! Well, I've done what I could.'

It was a sad moment. The sincerity of that embrace had been unmistakable. The king loved Magnus Brahe. In the year of his birth – 1757 – Brahe's father had gone to the block after an unsuccessful attempt at a revolution to increase the power of Gustaf's parents, the gentle King Adolf Fredrik and his imperious Queen Lovisa Ulrika.

Pechlin had been in such a hurry to get away from Gävle that he had departed while the Estates were still assembling for divine service in the Hall of State. Many other conspirators followed his example; they, too, wanted to get back to the capital as soon as possible. Ribbing and Kurck were driving their own horses and did not force the pace. Before reaching Älvkarleby they were overtaken by Anckarström. Several of the conspirators spent the night together in an inn, where they held a council of war. More and more of them were adhering to Ribbing's plan for a revolution.

That evening spirits ran high in the Nobles' club. Everyone accalimed Brahe and all the others who had spoken so adroitly on their behalf, and in a triumphant delirium they all went in a body to the lodgings of the Earl Marshal and tossed him in the air. A person of suspect political affiliations who had wormed his way in was sharply sent about his business; if he had resisted he would have been thrown out of the window. Thanks to the Earl Marshal's diplomatic guidance, all the dangers which had threatened their Estate had been set at naught. For their victory they had to thank their loyalty to each other, and their united attitude. Brahe treated his noble brethren to Hungarian wine and liqueurs.

Meanwhile, in Gävle Castle, quite another mood prevailed. The king was in a bad humour. When he set out next morning, he was in a tearing hurry. His farewells were taken without respect to rank or persons, Schröderheim and the royal entourage, at risk of broken legs, came rushing down the castle steps just in time to see the king hurriedly getting into his covered sledge.

'Drive on!' he shouted. And pulled up the wooden window slat.

Many a long mile of silent forests and endless plains lay ahead of him. Like most monarchs, Gustaf was merciless to his post horses. He liked to drive fast. Determined to arrive in time to see the play at the Bollhuset that evening, he did not even pause for rest at Östanå Inn at Alvkarleby; nor at Yvre, at Högsta, or at other posting inns where his sweating horses were released from their harness and instantly exchanged for fresh ones. Somewhere north of Uppsala the royal sledge-and-four forced another into the snow drifts. It was the sledge in which Captain Anckarström was travelling.

On Riddarhustorget Square in Stockholm the royalist brewer Abraham Westman was mingling with the crowd. Making authoritative statements about how well everything had gone off at Gävle, he had tried to prevail upon the cavalry of the National Guard to sit up late to receive the king. But the citizens who composed it did not share his view that all had gone well at Gävle; nor were they disposed to hide their dissatisfaction under hypocritical demonstrations of joy. On the contrary, the word was going round that when the king turned up at the theatre everyone should pretend not to see him.

About seven in the evening the royal equipage reached Haga, in the city's northern outskirts. In eleven hours it had put behind it the 102 miles from Gävle – an unusually swift piece of travelling, even by princely standards. Humanly speaking, its occupant should therefore have felt somewhat fatigued. But hastily changing his clothes, with hardly a moment's pause, the king drove straight in to town to see the play. At the Bollhus Theatre he was not accorded the usual burst of applause. Both pit and boxes received him with a coolness which astonished him. In the theatre were numbers of people on whom neither he nor his courtiers remembered having previously set eyes. It was a great disappointment. Gustaf regretted having driven so fast.

Immediately on his return from Gävle, Anckarström had gone to the gunsmith's to fetch his two pistols. They had been repaired. Several days went by without his seeing Ribbing. But he ran into Horn in the street. Horn thanked him for a couple of letters he had sent from Gävle.

'You were right,' Anckarström said. 'Nothing is being done *encore.*'

'As I'm always telling you,' rejoined Horn.

They parted company.

In the course of the next few days most of the conspirators returned to the capital. Only Thure Bielke and Jakob von Engeström stayed on in the country. Once again the old palace on Blasieholmen, where Regina Pettersson had resumed command of the general's household and the footman Lönngren was again keeping the door, became the conspirators' headquarters. One person whom Lönngren often had to admit was Ribbing. Lilliehorn came, too. Sometimes he had with him a young lieutenant on the artillery staff, by name Carl Fredrik Ehrensvärd. Like most of the artillery officers, this emotional idealist belonged to the opposition. He was a great enthusiast for the liberty and equality which had won such splendid victories in France, but which were being stifled here in his own fatherland. Ehrensvärd and Lilliehorn were intimate friends, Ehrensvärd being full of admiration for his older friend's moral rectitude.

Almost daily a coterie of nobles sat down to dinner at Pechlin's table. One was Ensign Peter von Plomgren, a boy of twenty who lived in the house and was a close relative of the general, whose wife had been a Plomgren. Others were Lieutenant Mikael von Strussenfelt, Captain Stålhammar and Hans Hierta, an eighteen-year-old clerk in the offices of the Chancelry. General Pechlin was his maternal uncle and his chief was Jakob von Engeström.

Hierta was too young to be initiated into all their closely guarded plans and secrets, but his revolutionary ardour was not less than the others'. He knew how to write verses which alluded savagely to the mismanagement of the country and the abuse of power. And there were plenty of subjects worthy of a satirist's lash. After Lönngren, the footman, had gone round the table with the wine decanter and Mamsell Regina was sure he was out of earshot, Hans Hierta would hand out copies of his verses, which the company would then sing – like other table songs of the Stockholmers, whether political or not – to some well-known melody.

A couple of days after his visit to the Bollhus Theatre the king went to the Opera. The curtain was so late in going up that the pit, who had to wait for the monarch, began to stamp. Although a long while had passed since his arrival, he was still lingering in his little cabinet. Once again he was not greeted by the usual burst of applause. After the performance, supping as usual in the intimate circle of his 'fondlings' (as his cavaliers were scornfully called) in the Royal Suite, Gustaf read out a letter he had just received from the Empress of Russia. Catherine promised on certain conditions to support his scheme for invading France and so come to the aid of the Bourbons. As they listened, the men around the king became deeply troubled. So – Gustaf still had not abandoned his crazy project; a project which would cost the country more rivers of blood and probably, no matter how well the *riksdag's* decisions had been managed, ruin it. And spring was not many weeks away. In a month's time the ice would melt and the highseas fleet perhaps be put into commission.

On the morning of Friday, 2 March, an advertisement appeared in the columns of *Dagligt Allehanda:* at the Opera that evening there was to be a masked ball. The news took the conspirators by surprise. Masked balls were unusual in Lent, and since no one knew whether there would be any others, they had no time to lose. Lieutenant Ehrensvärd went to Ribbing's lodgings on Drottninggatan, and found Ribbing had just been reading the advertisement. He was excited.

'Here's a chance we mustn't lose! Now for the revolution!'

'By putting the king out of the way?' wondered Ehrensvärd. Ribbing nodded. 'Anckarström has told me he's going. Is the garrison to be relied on?'

'I think so. That's to say, providing the revolution is sensibly carried out and the garrison receives proper orders.'

Though Ribbing was only two years older than the twenty-five-year-old Ehrensvärd, he had already been promoted captain. Enthusiastically, he began explaining why it was such a good opportunity, even though there was no time for elaborate preparations. As yet the troops with their royalist officers and carefully selected other ranks which had been sent to Gävle had not had time to return to the capital. The corps of dragoons and the Blue and Yellow

Guard, so Ribbing had heard, were still at Märsta, eighteen miles north of Stockholm. The Second Life Guards, who had left Gävle a day earlier, were expected that same afternoon or evening. Admittedly, this seemed ominous. All the officers of this new regiment were commoners, and therefore, from the insurgents' point of view, the least to be relied on. But after their long march the soldiers would be tired and were therefore nothing to fear. But the artillery was crucial. All live ammunition was kept at its barracks. The conspirators had to be quite sure of the artillery.

As Ribbing and Ehrensvärd were going into town together they happened to run into Lilliehorn, the lieutenant-colonel of artillery who had been the conspirators' supreme commander in Stockholm during the Gävle *riksdag*. Ribbing urged Enrensvärd to tell Lilliehorn about their hasty decision. But Lilliehorn was going in another direction.

Ehrensvärd therefore accompanied Lilliehorn to Riddarhustorget Square. It was dinner time, so they went into a restaurant called Hoffstens to have a bite to eat. They agreed that, should anything happen, Lilliehorn was to inform Ehrensvärd, and, providing they received orders from the queen, they would try to hold the Artillery Barracks in the Ladugårdslandet suburbs. While still busy discussing this scheme, they saw the artillery major, von Hartsmansdorff, coming in. He was Ehrensvärd's superior. Immediately they got up from their table and drew him over to the window.

'Tonight something is going to be undertaken against the king at the masquerade,' Ehrensvärd said in a low voice. 'It's best to be *careful*, in case something should happen.'

Hartsmansdorff was a man in his fifties. Astonished he looked from one to the other. Before the *riksdag*, he had promised Pechlin that, in the event of the king resorting to violence to force through certain illegal measures at Gävle and a revolution breaking out, he would help Lilliehorn to pacify the capital. But this new action, to be undertaken at such short notice, worried him.

'I can't promise anything unless Gyllengranat agrees,' he said.

'If he gets orders he'll have to agree.'

Colonel Gyllengranat was the commander of the brigade of artillery. The plan was that, after the king had been murdered, the artillery, on orders from the queen, should be placed at the disposition of the Crown Prince. All they knew of Gyllengranat was that he was not altogether negative towards the plan. Though he did not want to join in any plot as long as the present king was on the throne, in the event of the coup d'état being successful he was willing to take orders from the new revolutionary government.

Others too were being informed of what was in the wind. Ribbing saw to it that Pechlin was told. Anckarström himself asked Horn to go to the masquerade. Horn, no friend of such pleasures, found it difficult to refuse. So he sent his servant out to Huvudsta with a message to the effect that he would not be home as early as usual. A woman friend, he alleged, had prevailed on him to go with her to the masked ball.

For one so happily married as Horn this was a clumsy alibi. His countess thought it strange that he should prefer another woman's company to her own, particularly as his delicate state of health was not usually equal to staying up all night at masquerades. In her reply she implored him to come home to Huvudsta before nightfall. And Horn obeyed. And let down his comrades.

Lilliehorn, for his part, was seized with anxiety. In the afternoon he went to see Pechlin and gave him Ribbing's message. The old man, who knew about it already, had no objections:

'There have been plenty of people here on the same errand,' he said, but mentioned no names. 'But what surprises me is that among the whole lot of them there isn't one who is prepared to do it out of pure love of liberty. They're all seeking revenge for private injustices.'

In the event, none of these precipitate arrangements came

to anything. At Anckarström's request Ribbing went to the masquerade, but seeing no mask that might be the assassin's, did not stay long. Yet Anckarström had been there, both masked and armed; but there had been so few other people at the masquerade he had not dared to shoot the king. He regarded the poor attendance as due to the advertisement being inserted only at the last minute.

When they met afterwards he told Ribbing: 'You'll have to get more people next time.'

That Friday, the day of the poorly attended masquerade, Baron Thure Stensson Bielke met Councillor Alegren at Rotebro Inn. They sat down to have dinner together. Both were on their way home to Stockholm from the *riksdag*. The councillor had attended as representative plenipotentiary for the city of Stockholm. On his way home Bielke had looked in on his sister.

'Now you've really something to be proud of, raising taxes by that regulation about bank coin!' said the baron, ironically. For some years he had known Alegren to be a reliable patriot; and the *riksdag*'s decision that part of everyone's taxes must be paid in coin of the realm was something which had also in high degree annoyed Alegren.

Bielke happened to mention his servant Johan, said he was more needed down on his farm in Södermanland than in town, and wondered whether Alegren could find him a decent fellow to run errands for him. Some servant of the city court, perhaps? The councillor had one to suggest – a porter in the police office.

'Couldn't I look you up in Stockholm, Councillor?' wondered Bielke, as they left the table to continue their journeys.

'You are welcome, Baron,' said Alegren.

The purpose behind that visit was not so innocent as might have appeared. Alegren knew very well what was in the wind and was willing to put himself at the conspirators' disposal. Should the need arise – and that, perhaps, would not be long now – he was also in a position to ensure a supply of reliable people from among the many dissatisfied citizens.

After his return to Stockholm, Bielke's visits to General Pechlin began to occur thick and fast. Anxiously he trotted out his theory that, unless a change was brought about, the nobility stood to lose both property and status. Enthusiastically he boasted of the revolutionary atmosphere prevailing among the citizenry. Bielke's talkativeness and his wild confused ideas exhausted Pechlin. Sometimes he thought the fellow must be out of his wits. As his host followed him to the door, Bielke said gaily:

'Now I'm going to my "old women and townsfolk".'

It was an enigmatic remark; but Pechlin knew what he meant by it.

Nor was Alegren idle. Knowledge of what was to come was spreading like ripples on a pond.

The thermometer had long hovered around zero. Suddenly, at the beginning of the following week, it fell sharply. On Tuesday night there was a gale accompanied by a heavy fall of snow, and the thermometer registered at least minus twenty-five degrees Celsius – extremely cold, even for Sweden. And so it remained. Over all the chimneys of Stockholm's mansard roofs the smoke hung in the air like candy-floss, while below the Slaughterhouse Bridge and the new bridge over the Stream, still not even half completed, the gulls squabbled above the patches of black unfrozen water. No one went out of doors who did not have to.

In *Dagligt Allehanda* for Wednesday the citizens of Stockholm could read that on Friday, 9 March, there was to be another masked ball. The pious might object to such worldly pleasures in Lent. The authorities simply ignored them.

This time the conspirators had more time to lay their plans. The same procedure was repeated, the only difference being that on Thursday it was Ribbing who took the initiative and went to Anckarström's house in Gamla Kungsholmsbrogatan.

Entering, he shouted:

'There's to be another masquerade!'

'Very well, then,' said Anckarström. 'Then it must happen. Whether many people are there or few.'

'We'll meet at the Opera!'

Ribbing met Lilliehorn in an eating house and went home with him to his house on Norrmalmstorg. There was to be a *coup* against the High Personage, he informed him. Once again Lilliehorn promised to place the guards at their disposal, should anything happen to the king, and in his turn warned the second-in-command of the artillery, Major von Hartmansdorff.

Friday dawned. Out of the blue March sky the sunshine flooded down over the town as it had been doing for the last three days; and still the extreme cold showed no signs of ending. Towards evening a notice was affixed to the closed doors of the Opera House. The cold being so severe, it announced, the masquerade had been cancelled. Anckarström shook the shot out of his pistols, and next time he met him on the street, Ribbing said in a disappointed tone of voice:

'Well, so there's to be no masquerade.'

'No. And they say there aren't to be any more, either. It's too late in Lent. Not that that bothers him. If only he doesn't go away – the king, that is.'

The cancellation of the masked ball certainly came as a great disappointment. In its wake followed anxiety, and anxiety, spreading among the conspirators, turned into fear. Even, here and there, into terror.

At first the murder plot had been an affair between the strong-willed Anckarström and the enthusiastic Horn. Then Ribbing had joined them. The two counts had doubted whether anything would really happen – perhaps deep down inside themselves had not even dared to imagine such a thing becoming a reality. They had joked with the man who said he would do it; sometimes they had egged him on to despise his victim. It was these three who had formed the action group, and it had been to their fumbling attempts old Pechlin had given his blessing. Such had been the state of affairs at the new year. Likewise during the *riksdag*, when prudence had restrained the assassin's pistol.

But now – the situation was quite different! It was becoming impossible to keep Ribbing's project secret. By now many people knew about it, and still more must do so if the revolution was to succeed. Nor was the conspiracy confined to the capital. In all the provincial towns of Sweden people were waiting for 'something to happen'. Officers of provincial regiments. Civil servants. Landlords on their estates. In the pockets of their skirts their wives, no less subversive than themselves, were hiding pamphlets critical of the government. Some noblemen had gone to the main provincial towns, to await the post from the capital. They wanted to know the moment the signal was given for revolt.

But now this damned cold was putting a spoke in everyone's wheel! Things had gone too far, and there was no drawing back. A single careless word from some chatterbox of a lackey or maidservant only had to reach the ears of the redoubtable Liljensparre, and they knew all too well what they could expect: lightning arrests, remorseless interrogations, the confessions of the weaker brethren, the capture of the guilty and then – squares of bayonets massed around scaffolds.

Little of this anxiety, however, was visible on the surface. Life went on as usual. Hoar frost glittering on their coats, horses pulled loads of hay through the city customs barriers, brewers' drays thundered over the Blue Sluice, sledge-drivers yelled out to pedestrians to mind their backs. In the evenings the ragged drunks of Stockholm staggered from tavern to tavern, while in the windows of brothels the pale rouged faces of girls waited for one or another penniless clerk to come along and, for the few pennies he had, beg from them the joy of living in the 'little death'.

The king, for his part, had other things to think of than the internal quarrels over the rate of exchange and credit notes. On Monday, 12 March, the courier brought a letter from Bergstedt, the first secretary of the Paris embassy. He told how young Count Fersen, who had been staying in Brussels after the French king's and queen's flight had been ignominiously stopped at Varennes, had suddenly reappeared in Paris, disguised as the lackey of another Swedish nobleman. This nobleman had brought a letter to the King of Portugal, signed by Gustaf III. Fersen had gone to a lot of trouble to forge the royal signature. The document was to save his life, should the revolutionary police seize him and ask for his papers. Fersen had even slipped into the Tuileries where he had met Louis XVI and Marie Antoinette. Afterwards he had asked Bergstedt to provide both himself and his companion with a courier's papers.

The king's eyes lit up with delight. He could have found no bolder emissary than 'Tall Fersen'. Once back across the frontier, he could be sure Fersen would send him a detailed report of his political negotiations with Louis and Marie Antoinette. Fersen was planning another attempt at flight.

Hearing this letter read out to the king, Baron Evert Taube, under-secretary of state for foreign affairs, Gustaf's most intimate adviser on French matters and the keenest advocate of a military intervention, fell into a panic. Had not Fersen written to him only a few days before that any further journey to Paris was out of the question? Even '*Elle*' – the Queen – when she had heard that visas were to be required of all travellers, had advised her *ami* against it. If Fersen should be unmasked, it would mean certain death – and the blame would be laid at the door of Gustaf III.

Now the weather came to the aid of the conspirators. On Monday it was still very cold. The day was bright and sunny and in the evening the northern lights illumined the sky. But on Tuesday it clouded over and a thaw set in; at the same time there were occasional falls of snow. On that day, to their relief, the conspirators were able to read in *Dagligt Allehanda* that there was to be a masquerade at the Opera on Friday, 16 March, starting at half-past ten. The arrangers, it seemed, were keen to get a public. The advertisement appeared three times.

The news shook the revolutionaries out of their stupor. Immediately Ehrensvärd was sent off as their courier to the north. Another courier was Ingemund Liliestråle, who went to Säby Manor – a dozen or so miles north-west of Stockholm – where his father, a former chancellor of justice, now in the autumn of his days, was busy translating English poets into laboured Swedish verse. In 1789 the old man's opposition to the king's tyrannous tendencies had cost him, too, some weeks' imprisonment; and when in town he paid occasional visits to Pechlin, who shared his views. Ingemund Liliestråle went on up into the Bergslagen district, as far as the city of Falun, the provincial capital of Dalarna. Another courier went to Kiplingeberg, north of Uppsala, where Jakob von Engeström had been lingering after his stay at Gävle. Hurriedly stuffing his papers into his suitcase, von Engeström left his estate. Late that evening he was back in Stockholm, in urgent need of Pechlin's and Lilliehorn's counsel.

On Thursday morning Anckarström met Ribbing in the street.

'I'm having dinner out at Huvudsta.'

'Give them my regards and tell them I'll be there at four o'clock,' Ribbing said.

'That's good. We'll be able to talk about tomorrow's masquerade.'

Anckarström's wife was staying with friends in the country and his oldest daughter had been taken care of by his Huvudsta friends. So his kitchenmaid Elsa Tyberg and the housemaid Anna Norberg did not find it strange when they saw the captain put on his overcoat and walk out to Huvudsta in the lightly falling morning snow to see his daughter.

There were several other guests at that dinner. One was Lovisa Hierta, who was hoping soon to become Ribbing's wife, and who in the new year had lent the conspirators her box at the Opera. Another was Count Wilhelm Dohna, a lieutenant of Light Dragoons who was stationed with his company out at Drottningholm, where he was responsible for mounting guard over the palace. Such an officer could be most useful. That day, flatly disregarding orders, he had ridden out to Huvudsta with a dragoon to meet Horn. So he was invited to dinner too.

It was an important meeting. The others were only too pleased to accept Ribbing's leadership. Their eyes fastened on his features, enthusiastic under the revolutionary hair-style. They went through the plan in detail. All were to meet at the Opera. Anckarström, for his part, promised to obtain a mask and domino outfit for Horn, who was to change that evening in Anckarström's room and thereafter accompany him to the scene of action. While they, together with others engaged for the purpose, crowded round the king, the shot was to be fired. For that Anckarström, alone, was to be responsible. And if he were caught red-handed or killed in the ensuing tumult, the counts promised to look after his wife and children and save them from poverty. Since they obviously could not discuss such matters in the presence of the other guests, there was no time for the three men to go through all the plans; so Ribbing suggested they meet again at his house on Friday morning.

From Huvudsta Ribbing drove in to Pechlin's house. He found many people gathered in the drawing-rooms. There was Bielke, with his crooked body, gesticulating wildly as he conversed with Jakob von Engeström. Plomgren and Strussenfelt, those regular hangers on at Pechlin's table, were considering which women could most suitably be invited to the masquerade. Pechlin himself was in a good mood, smacking his lips over his glass and sucking at his eternal pipe. Sometimes he would pluck one of his guests by the sleeve, and draw him into his bedroom.

No one noticed that for his part Lieutenant-Colonel Lilliehorn mostly sat brooding, giving curt replies to all questions. Everyone realized how heavy his responsibilities must lie on him if this revolution, after so many abortive attempts, were to succeed. Lilliehorn's features betrayed no sign of what he was thinking: but when he got home to his apartment on Norrmalmstorg, late that evening, he sat down at his writing desk and took out pen and paper.

V

RIBBING TAKES OVER

At half-past six in the morning Anckarström got out of bed. He lit his own fire in the tiled stove in the corner of the room, and while waiting for it to burn up stood looking out of the window. Yesterday's fall of snow still lay white and pure on the rooftops and in the confined space of the yard.

About eight o'clock he went over and breakfasted with his children. Then, going back to his room, he considered the things he would have to get hold of during the day. His reflections were disturbed by a visit from one of his closest friends, Captain Carl Johan Gyllencreutz. The latter's affairs lay in serious disorder and Anckarström had indicated that he would be prepared to loan him money. But just now he had not enough ready cash.

Many hours were to pass before evening, and after Gyllencreutz had gone Anckarström was too agitated to stay by himself in his room. To pass the time, he went out and for a long while he strolled about the streets. At length he went up to Gyllencreutz' cousin, Lieutenant-Colonel Alf Gyllencreutz, a relation by marriage. The two men sat down to have a chat, and Anckarström suggested that the other should help his cousin by lending him the money. Had he not just inherited a fortune from his father-in-law? And there they sat, talking, until it was time for Anckarström to go home and have dinner. Just then he recalled his promise to Horn, and went to Hartin's the hatmakers on Helgeandsholmen, near the old bridge over the Stream. There he bought a mask for 32 shillings and asked to hire two of the black domino outfits which the shop assistant laid out in front of him.

'That'll be 32 shillings each,' the boy told him. And began writing out a bill.

Anckarström threw down a ten riksdaler note and went off, the parcel of clothes under his arm.

All that morning Lilliehorn's thoughts had revolved around the letter he had begun writing the previous evening. His conscience gave him no peace. More and more, he felt the absolute necessity of preventing this crime. But how despatch the warning? Supposing he went out to Haga, asked for an audience, and boldly exposed the whole plot? The king, perhaps, would believe him, even without any evidence. And his life would be saved – for the time being. But it would be utterly impossible to keep secret the name of the man who had warned him. By his friends, by conspirators, by the entire aristocracy and nobility of Sweden he, Lilliehorn, the man whom everyone had held in such high esteem, would be regarded as a low informer, a traitor to liberty; rejected as an outcast. So – there was nothing for it. The letter would have to be anonymous. He still had time to consider how it could best be delivered.

Once again Lilliehorn sat down at his writing desk. His anxiety was calmed somewhat by the regular rows of gold-embossed calf-leather bindings which embraced him in his library. It was not yet time to go to his meeting at the military tribunal. The morning was his. Critically, he read through what he had written:

To the King – in all deference.
Permit an unworthy man, nameless, but whose pen is dictated by the voice of duty and conscience, to dare to take the liberty of informing You with all frankness that both in the provinces and here in town are persons who breathe such hatred and revenge against You that they will not stick in one way or another to cut off the thread of Your life by murder.

Lilliehorn knew the king had often received anonymous warning letters. Usually, after glancing through them, Gustaf threw them away. It was important therefore that the opening lines should really capture his attention.

He went on:

> In despair when they saw the last masked ball go wrong, they are delighted to see another announced for today (thieves of the night, it is said, eschew streetlamps). Nothing is better suited to treacherous attacks than darkness and disguise. By all that is most sacred I therefore presume to implore You to put off this damnable ball until a more suitable time, with respect both to Your own present and future interests, and also out of consideration for some headstrong persons, out of whose hands the good God, bringing them to their senses, may one day wrest the dagger.

There! The scene of the planned assassination had been stipulated. Such information, Lilliehorn thought, must give the king greater pause. If a plan existed which should have been put into effect at some earlier date, but had been made impossible by the extreme cold, such a plan must necessarily have ripened in the interim, and this must increase the chances of the king paying serious heed to his warning; likewise make him wonder who the writer of the letter could be. Now he must find some phrases to avert suspicion from his own person.

> I have the honour to assure You, with Heaven as witness of the mainspring and purity of my intentions, that the message I have now given You comes from one who is no courtier, who is in no need of anything, but is far from approving all the errors You have committed, both in respect to the war, in politics, and above all in morals.

No courtier! Himself he was a nobleman who from his earliest years had been brought up at court and all of whose expenses had been paid out of the king's privy purse. It was an obvious lie; but what he wrote about his dissatisfaction over the war, politics and morals came from the depths of Lilliehorn's heart. Morals! If the king had kept a mistress, as all princely personages in every age have been in the habit of doing, no one would have criticized him. But he was happiest among his 'fondlings'. The strangest rumours were flying about concerning the sort of life being lived at court. Not even in the brothels of Baggensgatan, it was said, were such passions loose. Only recently he had heard that the king had invited the actress Mamsell Frédérique Löf and an actor out to Haga, and there ordered them to dance naked and play the whore together; after which he and the gentlemen of his chamber had toyed with them until they were exhausted. Even if that rumour was nothing but slander, Gustaf was worse than Heliogabalus, that most depraved of all the Roman emperors.

Again Lilliehorn put pen to paper. He must get on with his letter. The lie about himself not being a courtier was not enough. Further red herrings were needed:

When I now in all frankness make this confession, it must seem so much the less suspect in Your eyes inasmuch as I can assure You that while I was at Gävle for the *riksdag* I should not for an instant have hesitated to draw my rapier to fight Your legionaries to the death if, as for a time seemed probable, the soldiery had at Your orders resorted to brute force.

Another lie. He had not been in Gävle for the *riksdag*. But his pen ran on and the lie became truth; for the military action which he alleged he would have been prepared to set in motion at Gävle was identical with what he had promised Pechlin to do in the capital.

You should therefore realize what a difference exists between the behaviour of a man of honour and firm mind and that of a low fellow who lets his feelings run away with him. The one sends up burning prayers for the general good and to that end desires nothing better than to resort to such methods as are dictated by religion and feelings of honour: while the other will stop at nothing.

Lilliehorn had only intended to write a short note; but his love of argument ran away with him and inveigled him into verbosity. He must extend the implications of his warning. More than just that evening's particular threat was in question:

However difficult, not to say impossible, it would be in the long run to warn You of all the dangers piling up about You, unless by a complete change of behaviour You make an effort to become reconciled with the sounder part of the nation, I have nevertheless regarded it as my duty towards You, and as a matter of my own satisfaction, to expose this fateful secret which, only a few hours ago, has come to my ears. I implore you, believe me; no imaginary fears drive me to this step, but, on the contrary, absolute certainty as to the reality of the matter of which I have been informed. Further, I implore You to take care when on the ground floor at Haga, which is especially well-suited to surprise attempts. If You repose the least confidence in me, You will cancel, at least until after the holidays, all masquerades whatever. The matter is of such great import not only to Yourself but also to us, that You must not plead Your own courage, which is unimpeachable. We know how boldly You dared meet the enemy. Therefore, without the least blemish to Your honour, You may seek to elude the assault of a traitor.
I shall always send up prayers for Your welfare, but I beg You do not institute any inquiries into the authorship of this letter. It is but labour lost, inasmuch as I have not spoken with any, but have been entirely alone in writing it.

Lilliehorn had written his draft in French. Now he immediately set to work to write out a fair copy in Swedish. Again he used his lead pencil, writing in large angular letters. After which he sealed the letter with his signet ring. Just as he had done so, his servant Krantz knocked at the door, and announced Jakob von Engeström. Stuffing the letter into his pocket, Lilliehorn received his guest. Not with a single word did he indicate his change of mind. On the contrary, he expressed great enthusiasm for the change in regime now to occur.

Jakob von Engeström had worries. To an experienced civil servant with a reputation for thoroughness, so brief a period of preparation seemed altogether too short. In the king's removal he wished to play no part. It was the ensuing measures which seemed so unclear. Which military commanders were to be relied on? Already, on Wednesday evening,

Lilliehorn and he had discussed this question; but for Engeström verbal proposals were not enough. He wanted to have everything on paper. Who might have to be arrested? Armfelt, of course. And Taube. Perhaps also the commander-in-chief of the artillery, General Sinclair? And who were to make up the new government – the council of state, now to be revived? Councillor Rosen? General Fredrik Horn? General Johan Didrik Duvall? All these were experienced men, and their inclusion would secure the public's confidence. Perhaps Thure Bielke would be the best man to look after the country's finances, in lieu of Håkansson? And he himself to take charge of foreign affairs?

These were crucial questions, and if the revolution was not to lead to chaos they had to be settled before evening. To all this Lilliehorn replied by reminding him that they were both invited to dinner at Pechlin's, where the final decisions were to be taken. Engeström decided to go home and draw up a memorandum.

About eleven o'clock Ribbing arrived outside the general's house and ran swiftly up the steps. The old man received him in a cloud of tobacco smoke. Drawing him into his bedroom, he closed the door.

Ribbing's resolution put new courage into the old man. After all these half-hearted attempts he had begun to have his doubts. He admitted frankly, however, that it would have been impossible to do anything at the masquerade of 2 March. There had been too few people. Now Anckarström had promised to act; and Horn had promised to support him, if not with deeds, at least with his advice. The liberties of the nation were to be restored, order was to be brought into its finances, and the key positions were to be filled with able persons instead of worthless favourites and fortune-hunters. Pechlin assured Ribbing that he, for his part, was ready to make a revolution at any moment. The Old Guard, the artillery, the Queen Mother's Regiment, all were to be relied on. Also the citizenry – Bielke was to see to that. In addition to all this they had reserves stationed in various parts of the country: the nobles and the regimental officers. Any moment now Ehrensvärd and Liliestråle should be back in town, after relaying the signal for action.

'But get me five or six men who will do as leaders,' the old man muttered.

That was more than Ribbing could promise. It was a task, he thought, for the other conspirators: Lilliehorn, or Jakob von Engeström. For his part, all his thoughts were focused on the masked ball. He implored the old man to gather as many people as possible. Pechlin promised to do so.

Just as Ribbing was leaving, he met Regina Pettersson out in the drawing-room.

'I'll be coming to dinner this evening,' he called out to her. And the mamsell thought she detected a note of triumph in his voice.

It was now the fourth morning in succession that the thermometer had risen a few degrees above zero. After the long period of severe cold people had a feeling of spring in the air – that spring which in any other country would still be called winter, but which is nevertheless a time of milder air and melting snows. A light south-easterly breeze was blowing. The morning had been overcast; but now the clouds were breaking up. That morning the king, out at Haga, had given audience to Lord Chancellor Wachtmeister. Wachtmeister's business had not been of the most agreeable. That very day the city court had begun to try a case of forgery, the forger being no less a person than Adolf Munck, the Master of the King's Horse and for many years a member of the king's and queen's most intimate circle. Gustaf had been depressed, spoken of the Ides of March, which troubled him as they once had troubled Julius Caesar. But after breakfast, accompanied by his duty officer, Captain Gustaf Löwenhielm of the Light Dragoons, the king had gone up into the forest above the pavilion to inspect his projected Corinthian-style palace. Already work on it had now progressed to a point where the foundations of the walls and the deep vaulted cellars had been laid out. The two men stood contemplating the enormous and costly project.

'When can one imagine New Haga being ready?' Löwenhielm asked.

'If I live as long as most men,' the king replied, 'I should have time to live in it a few years.'

From the lake of Brunnsviken, nearby, a sound of sleighbells and cries made itself heard. The trotting races had begun. As usual, competitors and onlookers had assembled at nearby Stallmästaregården; after which the sleighs had taken a turn on the ice. The king and Löwenhielm drove over to see the race. Finding Carl Didrik Hamilton, one of his courtiers, among the onlookers by the frozen lakeside, he commanded him to go to Duke Charles and his duchess and invite them to the masquerade, together with his sister the Princess Sofia Albertina. Hamilton was invited to sup with the duchess.

As they went flying over the snow in their sledges, the young officers and civil servants, catching sight of the king, put their heads together and spoke of matters not suited to be heard by all ears. Many had already agreed to gather in cafés and clubs that evening, there to await events. They belonged to the many-branched brotherhood of the aristocratic conspiracy. Their whips cracked. Before another morning dawned, so, they knew, would a pistol.

On the main road into the city from the north a horse came trotting in towards the Norrtull barrier. It was drawing a sledge. In the sledge sat Lieutenant Ehrensvärd, and beside him sat the clerk, Ingemund Liliestråle, who had been given a lift from Säby. After his long journey through Bergslagen, he had met Ehrensvärd there on the previous evening, in the home of his aged parents. As the town drew closer the lieutenant said:

'I believe someone has a *dessein* against the king today.'

Even if Liliestråle knew what plans were afoot, it sent cold shivers through him to think that the time had now been fixed for the deed.

'Do you know who it is?' he asked. His voice trembled.

'No. Nor when it's to happen.'

'Tell me nothing,' Liliestråle implored his companion. 'It's best I hear nothing from your lips.'

By about midday they were in town. Their ways were about to part – Liliestråle was to seek out a certain Count Douglas on urgent business. But Ehrensvärd was loth to let the other man out of his sight. 'Where are you dining today?' he asked.

'I haven't decided yet. Mostly I dine at a relation's. And you?'

'I think I'll go to General Pechlin's.'

'I'd like to come with you. I've heard one is always welcome there, even uninvited.'

'Do so. We'll meet there.'

Liliestråle went to change his clothes, while Ehrensvärd went to the National Debt Office and sought out Bielke, who embraced him with great heartiness. He, too, was to go to Pechlin's.

The guests had been invited for two o'clock, the hour when the wealthy dined. But long before that, Hans Hierta had turned up. The lad had hurried in to his cousin Peter von Plomgren and there had met Mikael von Strussenfelt. All three were to go to the masked ball and had already obtained black domino costumes. Now the other guests arrived. Here came Adolf Ribbing, Jakob von Engeström, Thure Bielke and Samuel Gustaf Hermelin, who had associated a great deal with Pechlin during the Gävle *riksdag*. Uninvited though he was, Ingemund Liliestråle, too, had plucked up courage to come to Pechlin's. Then, just as the general was calling them to table and offering them a glass of schnapps, Lilliehorn arrived, followed by Ehrensvärd, also self-invited. Pechlin had not been counting on so many guests. Two more places had to be hastily laid for them.

It was a gay, even uproarious dinner. Mamsell Regina was hostess. The general's witty sallies threw them all into fits of laughter; and all the time no mention was made of any matter of importance, so the customary arrangement whereby the older servants were not allowed to serve at table seemed a trifle superfluous. But the household stuck to its habits. When Mamsell Regina rang her bell, the eleven-year-old page, Nisse Åberg, brought in plates and dishes and cleared away with an efficiency no one would have believed possible in a mere peasant lad.

Mamsell Regina Pettersson had been looking after the widower's household for seven years. To her chagrin she had not had a chance to attend a single masquerade all that winter, though masked balls were her favourite pleasure. Encouraged by the young officers, she asked the general for permission to accompany them this evening.

A long while Pechlin studied her out of his screwed-up, cunning, ever-blinking eyes:

'Not worth the trouble,' he said, and cut short her entreaties.

Pechlin took great care of his mamsell. Not only did she know how to keep little Nisse, old Lönngren and the maids in the kitchen in order: her cunning feminine tricks could be relied on to fend off all undesirable spies. Not for nothing was her bedroom next door to the general's. From her he had few secrets. Mamsell Regina went on nagging. The old man objected. But in the end gave in. Nisse, too, was given permission to go with them to the Opera, and take a look at all those queerly costumed 'masks'.

In this company Ingemund Liliestråle felt himself something of an outsider. He had no idea what to talk about. But then Bielke came over, and, drawing Liliestråle into one of the nearby rooms, began preaching a long sermon on the wretched state of the realm.

'Not for one minute can one feel sure there isn't going to be a catastrophe,' he asserted, emphatically. 'Not even on such a day as today.'

'What do you fear, then, Baron?'

'An *attentat* perhaps. Against the bank,' Bielke hastened to add; but did it with so secretive an expression on his face that Liliestråle doubted whether he really meant what he was saying.

'By whom?'

'My dear young sir, you will soon see. Promise to tell me if you should hear anything.'

All of a sudden the gay mood of the dinner party had evaporated. One by one Pechlin called his guests into his bedroom where, in a low voice, he spoke in turn with each. Ribbing was standing in a corner with Ehrensvärd. They had not seen each other since last Friday, the day of the anti-climax.

'I have now informed the general of everything. You're going to the masquerade?'

'Yes.'

'Black domino and square-toed boots. Remember. So we can recognize each other.'

While the guests were still drinking their coffee, Pechlin gestured to Lilliehorn to come into his room. Sitting down on a chair beside the bed, the general invited the lieutenant-colonel to sit down opposite him. At that moment Engeström, too, entered. Turning to Pechlin, he asked whether it wouldn't be better if the volunteers the general said he could get together were given the responsibility for maintaining order in the city until the troops had time to assemble.

Pechlin agreed. As usual, his speech was somewhat slurred, so that at times it was hard to make out clearly what he was saying. Now, for once, he abandoned his inveterate rule: never to discuss political matters except in a tête-à-tête.

Engeström took his memorandum out of his pocket:

'The queen is to be notified after all,' he said. 'We must appoint some people to do it, and act temporarily as her advisers.'

Pechlin named a few names.

'And then the council.' (Engeström used the French word *conseille*, not the Swedish word *råd*.) 'Unfortunately this matter is still unsettled. Councillor Rosén has been mentioned; and Generals Horn and Duvall.'

'It won't do!' The old man shook his silvery-grey wig energetically. 'No one has given them the least notice of this evening's entertainment.'

'Won't you give us your own nominations for the council, general?' asked Engeström, obsequiously. Lilliehorn, breaking silence, agreed – being so deep in this nasty business, he felt he must keep up appearances. But Pechlin would have nothing to do with it.

'No, no, I'm an old man and want to stay here in my own house. I can do most from here, it seems.'

This little exchange made Lilliehorn even more dubious than he had been before. Their ideas of what ought to be done, he thought, were decidedly immature, half-cocked. Getting up, he made ready to depart.

Now it was Ehrensvärd's turn to ask Liliestråle whether he meant to go to the masquerade.

Ingemund tried to wriggle out of it.

'I'm busy all this evening,' he said. 'As I've already told you, I've got to meet Count Douglas to draw up a lease before he leaves town. Anyway, I've no costume.'

'Hire one at Hartin's, then, or some other clothier's. If you have time I do hope you'll keep me company. Anyway, I'll pass by your house on my way to the masquerade.'

Hierta, Plomgren and Strussenfelt moved into Mamsell Regina's chamber, where there was a clavichord. As it happened, a young girl, by name Anna Johanna Unge, had come to pay Mamsell Regina a visit; so Lieutenant Strussenfelt invited her to accompany him to the masked ball. Had not Ribbing asked them to gather a lot of people? True, she was a bit on the young side, only sixteen; but young Hierta would make a suitable escort. Nor had he anything against doing so. They carefully avoided telling her that she wouldn't have a chance to dance many quadrilles.

Ehrensvärd was standing in the lobby, making his host many polite bows as he thanked him for his hospitality:

'Have you spoken to Ribbing, Baron?' the old man asked sharply.

'Yes.'

'And you're definitely going to the masquerade, Baron? And taking Liliestråle with you?'

'Yes.'

The old man smiled contentedly. A momentary gleam of good-humour lit up in his usually cunning old face. He liked these young subalterns who would undertake to carry a secret message quicker than a servant his mistress' *billets doux*. By now many people knew what was going to happen; and before the evening there would be even more. One group was to sit and wait at Lindberg's Inn, out in Djurgården Park. Another, in the cellar of the Opera House, one of the town's smarter eating places. These were folk he could rely on. What happened thirty-six years ago, when the late Queen Lovisa Ulrika tried to seize power, must on no account occur again. That time a degraded non-commissioned officer had given away the whole plot in his cups. Expensive drinks, those. Eight heads had fallen to the executioner's sword. Eric Brahe's, Horn's, Puke's . . .

Just as the guests were breaking up to go, another gentleman arrived. It was Anders Nordell, the district judge. On the south side of the town it was washing day, and his wife had asked him to have his dinner out. Which he had done, inviting himself to his friend, the brewer Isaac Westman. After which he had gone to inquire whether any letters had arrived for him, and at the new slaughterhouse, furthest out on Blasieholmen Island, had intended to take a boat across the Stream into town. Now he was in a hurry. At five he was to meet a bank manager on Riddarholmen to go on sorting out the estate of a recently deceased general. But before embarking, Pechlin being so close at hand, Nordell had thought he would look in on the old man and hear how he was. Besides, it was Friday. He could take a look at the latest news from Germany. Perhaps the general would offer him his usual glass of small beer and pipe of tobacco?

As Nordell came in, Lieutenant-Colonel Lilliehorn and his host were standing bowing to each other, prior to taking their leave, so he went over to the table and took a pipe. Filling it, he hardly had time for more than a whiff or two before the old man came stumping up to him.

'Where have you been all this time? I've hardly seen anything of you.'

In the days when he had lived in another part of Pechlin's palace, Nordell had dined regularly at his table; but after moving house to the south of the city last autumn, his visits had become more sporadic. A whole week had gone by since last time.

'I've been out on assizes,' Nordell said.

'Have you seen Secretary Engeström?'

Nordell and Johan von Engeström were neighbours in the south part of the town, so it was a reasonable question for Pechlin to ask. They associated a good deal.

'No, general; but if those are your orders I'll tell him.'

'Do so. And you will be so kind as to come here at ten o'clock this evening; and it wouldn't do any harm if you collected together a few friends around you, in time for this evening's meeting.'

Nordell knew perfectly well what 'meeting' was in question. The advance guard was calling on the reserves. This evening many little groups would be sitting playing cards or drinking innocent-seeming cups of tea in various parts of the city as they waited impatiently for the signal. Nordell's and Pechlin's conversation was interrupted by a little wizened old gentleman, with whom Nordell was not acquainted, coming into the room. So nothing more was said. Nordell put down his pipe, took his hat and hurried off down to the quay, where the woman who rowed the ferry would soon be pushing off.

As for Lilliehorn and Ehrensvärd, they had gone down the steps together, leaving Jakob von Engeström behind to put on his coat and leather galoshes; but by Mrs Brandell's little house he caught up with them. Together, the three men went along the waterside to Norrmalmstorg Square, outside the Opera House, where Engeström left them.

Ehrensvärd went up with Lilliehorn into his apartment. It was in the Kastenhof House, between Malmstorgsgatan and Regeringsgatan, and thus had the Opera House on its left. The second-in-command of the First Life Guards lived in the same house, so a sentry was always posted at the front door. Up to this point Ehrensvärd had been full of enthusiasm for the revolution; but now that the decision to murder the tyrant had irreversibly been taken, his enthusiasm had begun to wane. He remembered his promise to Lilliehorn:

'Can't I do my bit just as well if I stay out in the square? As soon as I hear the rumour I'll come up to you, just the same.'

'Too uncertain,' Lilliehorn objected. 'You must go to the masquerade, as I've said. You must see with your own eyes that it's happened. And then report to me.'

Lilliehorn spoke authoritatively. Nor had he any qualms about doing so. Had he not got the warning letter in his pocket? There was not going to be any murder. So there would be no mortal tidings tonight either for Ehrensvärd to bring.

When Ribbing got home, he found Anckarström sitting waiting for him. While the conspirators were dining at

Pechlin's he had been out in the town making some purchases. From a watchmaker, near his own dwelling, he had bought some files; but finding them not to his liking, had gone on to Stora Badstugatan on the south side, where he had bought another. Home again, he had sat down to file a barb in the big kitchen knife. After which it was time for his meeting. Not until about half-past five did Horn turn up. Hardly was he inside the door than he asked what old Pechlin had said.

'He has been informed of everything and is ready for action,' Ribbing replied. 'Bielke has collected masses of citizens, and there are to be still more.'

Horn seemed content with his reply.

'Was Lilliehorn there?' he asked.

'He came with Ehrensvärd. The old man asked me to get hold of five or six fellows who could be leaders, but that was something I couldn't undertake. It should be the other way round. I asked him to get together as many people as he could, so that the house shan't feel too empty. And he has promised to do so.'

His answer satisfied Anckarström. From his pocket Horn had taken out two pocket pistols. He laid them down. Anckarström frowned.

'Did the Huvudsta coachman see you bringing these?'

'He did.' Horn laughed nervously. 'No one at home was surprised, I'm always armed when I go back and forth. Didn't I tell you what happened to me last winter in Solna Wood?'

'Tramps?' said Ribbing.

'Yes, a couple of tramps threw themselves at me and tried to pull me out of my sledge with a rope. One of them was just going to hit me a blow with his fist, when my coachman, Engzell, saved me at the last moment with his whip. Since then I've always gone armed.'

'Are you taking them to the masquerade, too?' Anckarström wondered, finding one of the pocket pistols loaded.

'I may need them afterwards. We must reckon with a riot. But I shan't have them at the masquerade, you can be sure of that.'

The mere thought of taking any physical part in the bloody deed gave Horn the shivers. Ribbing, afraid that his friend Anckarström might lose courage, declared flatly:

'If it doesn't happen now, we'll all be caught.'

This was undeniable. So when Ribbing showed them his domino costume and his boots they paid close attention. He was to point out the victim to the assassin; it was important they should be able to recognize him in the crowd.

'I've square-toed boots,' he said.

Together, Horn and Anckarström went down to Drottninggatan. Now there was really no turning back. A murder can be committed by one man. But not a *coup d'état*. If a *coup d'état* is to succeed, many forces must be coordinated. At the conspirators' headquarters on Blasieholmen the decision had been taken and already the adjutants were on their way with the leaders' last instructions to the chiefs of the little groups, who in turn were to inform their subordinates. It it didn't happen now, they would all be discovered. The risk was great. But Anckarström was keeping a cool head and gave no sign of hesitation. After leaving Horn in the street, he went to pass a couple of hours in the company of his friend Captain Gyllencreutz. But Horn was more anxious. Supposing the royalist-minded mob went berserk and it came to blows? Would his pocket pistols be enough? No – he must have a sabre. Without cold steel he would never manage. A sabre he must have.

Walking quickly, he hurried to Damström's the swordmaker's on Drottninggatan, only to hear to his annoyance that the shop had moved to Stora Vattugränd. Arriving there about six o'clock, he was immediately recognized by Damström.

'I want to borrow a sabre,' Horn told him. 'But it's got to

be sharp.'

'Sharp? I don't sharpen sabres in peacetime.' The old man thought it an odd request. Horn muttered something about his not having heard him properly, and began examining two sabres, exhibited in the window. Taking one of them, he half pulled it out of its scabbard; then drove it home again with a bang.

'It's not all that good, but it'll have to do.'

There was no more talk of its being sharpened. But Horn noticed the metal wires on the hilt were loose and wanted the fault rectified. Old Damström promised to have it done by eight o'clock that evening, after which Horn made off as quickly as he had come. This time he sought out Ribbing.

After his visit to Pechlin, Nordell had taken a boat over to the Old Town from the Skeppsholmen landing stage. From there he had gone on to Riddarholmen Island, but on his way had looked into Maja Lisa's coffee house, hoping to fall in with Secretary Netzell, a clerk in the foreign department, who had promised him to check the minutes of some meetings. He worked in the same office as Hans Hierta and they had become close friends. But there was no Netzell in the coffee house and instead he saw Nystedt, the deputy city procurator. Nystedt was sitting playing chess with a lawyer. Nystedt knew nothing of the conspiracy; and it occurred to Nordell, a cautious character, that it might not be a bad idea if he was seen in his company this evening – just in case everything went wrong and he had to prove the innocence of his own political affiliations.

'Care to come home with me?' he asked.

'By all means. But not before I've finished my game.'

Nordell asked the deputy-procurator to wait for him until his business on Riddarholmen was finished. That did not take long. Soon he was back at the coffee house. Together they went over to the south side. Nordell wanted Nystedt to help him adjust the minutes. On their way they passed by the house where Johan von Engeström lived. Nordell had to go upstairs and pass on Pechlin's message. While Nystedt waited in an outer room, Nordell took Engeström into an inner one.

'The old man wants to see you,' he said. 'They say there's to be a revolution tonight. Well, you're a nobleman and know that better than I.'

Johan von Engeström smiled. If anyone knew what was going to happen, surely it was Nordell, Anckarström's friend. But he promised to go to Pechlin at once.

'Pechlin wanted me, too, to come to him at ten this evening,' Nordell went on, 'but I don't feel up to it. Afterwards, when you've been there, you can tell me what the old boy said.'

After which Nordell went home with Nystedt and they absorbed themselves in checking the minutes. His wife was still busy doing her washing – after all, it was a perfectly ordinary weekday – and she had no time to lay the table for their supper. If they wanted something to eat, then they would have to go out and dine in a restaurant.

That evening it was many a man's lot to run the leaders' errands, to act, as it were, as adjutants on their staff. Councillor Alegren – he who, on his way back from Gävle, had had such a pleasant conversation with Baron Bielke about the excessive burden of taxation at the inn at Rotebro – had suddenly got visitors. An elderly gentleman was sitting in his room drinking small beer, smoking and reading an *Histoire de Naufrages* – a history of shipwrecks. Not exactly the most encouraging of reading matter – tonight they would need all their knowledge of the art of political navigation if they were to weather the impending storm.

Just as darkness was falling someone knocked at the front door. Taking a candle from his table, Alegren went downstairs and opened the door. The deputy notary of the city court, Gerhard Fredrik Enhörning, was standing outside. He wanted a word with him. Quietly Alegren let the notary into a little room on the ground floor.

'Are you going to the masked ball tonight?' was the urgent question.

Alegren couldn't say for certain. He had a visitor. Enhörning, a restless character, disappeared; but soon came back and repeated his question. This time Alegren was less negative. As soon as his guest had gone, he said, he would get ready and go with Enhörning. He already owned a mask, and somehow or other he would get hold of a domino outfit.

All this secrecy seemed a trifle superfluous. The name of the guest who was sitting absorbed in the history of shipwrecks was none other than Thure Stensson Bielke. He had come straight from Pechlin – to his 'old women and townsfolk', as he quaintly put it – with the very latest news. And now he left, to go back to Blasieholmen. A man who before sunrise would perhaps find himself responsible for the finances of the entire realm had many things to see to.

Yes, that Friday was an ordinary working day. But up at the Palace, in the offices of the president of the chancelry, people were working a great deal harder than in most other places. Here all the correspondence with Swedish embassies abroad was attended to, and since it was a post-day, the hastily scribbling secretaries could not leave their office until all mail had been packed up and sent down to the post office in Lilla Nygatan. While they were coding the letters with the aid of their cipher tables, Jakob von Engeström came in. This was not unusual. Many years earlier the old gentleman had served as a secretary to the president and afterwards it had been his habit to come up to the office with some letter or other which he wanted to despatch free of charge by the Hamburg courier.

But this particular evening Engeström behaved so strangely that the secretaries wondered what on earth could be the matter with him. At least one of them, Johan Albrekt Ehrenström, thought Engeström seemed oddly inquisitive. Pointing to one of the cupboards, he asked – as if to refresh his memory – which cupboard was called the secret one. Baron Rosenhane told him. Then he wondered who kept the key to that cupboard, and whether any night watchman kept guard in the outer room at nights?

Baron Rosenhane's answers were frank and straightforward; but all this unnecessary inquisitiveness on the part of a gentleman who no longer had anything to do with foreign affairs annoyed the others. None of them could guess that only a few hours earlier Jakob von Engeström, with the approval of Pechlin, had appointed himself minister for foreign affairs in the revolutionary government.

After this von Engeström went off to have supper with his sister-in-law, and thence to his own home, there quietly to await events. On his person he had his memorandum, with all the names.

By the time the foreign mail was all finally wrapped up and the exhausted civil servants could go home, darkness had fallen. Ehrenström was a man who in highest degree enjoyed the king's confidence. He was one of those who had signed the Peace of Värälä and who had accompanied the king on his journey to Aachen. So he had the clearest of consciences, and went early to bed. Masquerades and suchlike antics were not for him.

At first, Jakob von Engeström and Ehrenström found they were going the same way, and their servants went ahead to light their masters' way with their lanterns. In the outer courtyard of the Palace the two gentlemen fell in with Count Måns Stenbock, who shouted out to them:

'In the distance, gentleman, you looked like a funeral procession!'

They all burst out laughing and with lively comments on the macabre error the little procession went on down towards Storkyrkobrinken.

On the opposite side of the Stream from the Palace, on Norrmalmstorg Square, lights were shining in Lilliehorn's apartment. Lieutenant Ehrensvärd had not been the only person to visit him that evening. A royal secretary had come up, and immediately after him Schmiterlöv, one of the royal bodyguards. Next day he was to commence his round of duty in the king's entourage. At about eight o'clock, while these two were discussing matters touching the night's events with the lieutenant-colonel, they had seen the king driving in from Haga, where he had been all day. At a full gallop his equipage emerged from Fredsgatan into the square beneath their window. Long after it had swung on to the North Bridge and disappeared between the old houses on Helgeandsholmen Island in the direction of Mynttorget, they could still hear the sound of its sleigh bells.

Now Lilliehorn's visitors, having learnt what they wanted to know, had gone, and Lilliehorn was left standing alone at his window. On the other side of the Stream the long rows of windows in the immense square palace gleamed brilliantly in the darkness. In that palace he, an eighteen-year-old orphan, had commenced his service as a page at the time when the king had carried out *his* bloodless revolution. In Gustaf III he had thought he had seen mankind's benefactor; and more particularly his own. Later he had begun his military career in the Blue and Yellow Guard, shown himself a capable soldier, and formed the strictest notions of honour. He had fought boldly against the Russians in a war whose bloody and chimerical glories had snatched seventy thousand Swedes for ever from their ploughs and flung the country's finances into chaos. For all this the king alone was responsible – that king who three years ago by a second *coup d'ètat* had trampled on the liberties of his subjects.

What outrages were not to be expected from him in the future, what risky policies! But to get rid of him in this way, by a scoundrelly murder – no, that went against all Lilliehorn's humane ideas. He was filled with grief, mortification, despair of heart; and his resolve to cause the whole diabolical plan to misfire grew stronger.

He was still standing there, deep in thought, when Krantz, his footman, announced Johan von Engeström, brother of the self-elected minister for foreign affairs. The latter had just been to see Pechlin and had been given his marching orders. For the personnel in the National Debt Office it was vital to know that Baron Bielke would be the man who was to take charge of the national finances.

Distrait, Lilliehorn listened to the little fellow's verbose chatter. With an expression which to Engeström seemed mysterious, he said suddenly:

'What a pity things can't be improved without a great disaster. Well, Ribbing has wanted things this way, not me.'

Engeström felt disturbed to note such doubts in the chief military officer of the revolution. Himself, he had come to another point of view. As he saw things, the people are subject to no judge. The people are entitled to execute their own laws. If a king commits crimes so great as to jeopardize the public safety, then it is the people's natural right to protect their own lives by rendering him harmless. In such a case the people are fully within their rights in condemning him to death. Humanity, it is said, shudders at the sight of a king on a scaffold. But at a time when the axe is hanging over their own heads, they will gladly suffer the lesser shudders of tyrannicide.

Johan von Engeström left Lilliehorn's house to go to Nordell, as agreed. Nordell was sitting waiting for him. Immediately afterwards, Lilliehorn, too, put on his blue overcoat and walked the few yards over to Drottninggatan, where he asked to speak with Ribbing. But the servant told him he was out.

Meanwhile Lieutenant Ehrensvärd had had much to do. First, he had been in company with some tea-drinkers. Then he had gone to the Artillery Barracks, in Ladugårdslandet, and found out from the sentry where the keys to the ammunition store were kept. His inquiry caused no surprise; after all, he was himself an officer of artillery. After that, he had been to his superior, Major Hartmansdorff, who lived nearby. There many people had gathered and were passing the time over a game of cards. The guests were almost all officers – Major Wennerstjerna, the host's colleague in the Stockholm section of the Artillery Brigade; Captain Jean Bauman, of the Second Life Guards; Carl Schultz, a dismissed captain; and Adam Lorenz Stålhammar, a captain in the Kalmar Regiment. Hartmansdorff's brother, Carl Adolf, had also been there.

This was the action group of the revolution. When the moment came, they were to seize the Artillery Barracks. Both majors of the artillery regiment were there, so success was assured. The Artillery's assembly point was only a few yards away. And it was from there the first orders were to be issued.

Ehrensvärd left his sabre, his hat and his spurs ready for the moment after the masquerade, when the signal was to be given. He informed them of everything that had been said at Pechlin's dinner party. He meant to stay with them until ten o'clock. Then he would don his mask and fetch Ingemund Liliestråle on his way to the Opera.

And now they could only wait. There were many ways of passing the time. Over a game of cards for instance. Or drinking tea. Or listening to someone playing the clavichord, as the three young men Plomgren, Strussenfelt and Hierta were doing in Mamsell Regina's sitting room. Meanwhile little Anna Johanna Unge had gone home to Ladugårdslandet to change into her party dress.

Bielke appeared in the doorway. This evening he was as restless as could be. Only a few minutes ago he had been at Councillor Alegren's, reading about historic shipwrecks. Now here he was back again, asking Mamsell Regina for a bite to eat.

He was not the only one who was hungry; so she gave the kitchenmaid Inga Jönsdotter orders to prepare some tasty

King Gustaf III of Sweden; an oil painting made in the year of his death.

The murderer Jacob Johan Anckarström, from a contemporary engraving (*above right*), with General Pechlin (*above left*), the conspirators' figurehead and the only man to hold out against interrogation by Liljensparre (*below*), the ruthlessly efficient Chief of Police.

dish, meanwhile herself laying the table for the whole company in her own sitting room. Pechlin came in, but fancied nothing from the table. Sitting down in front of the tiled stove he began roasting apples.

On the south side of the town, Nordell and Nystedt had been checking their minutes for some time when Auditor Runeberg suddenly appeared; and, on his heels, Prosecutor Ternell. The two men had agreed to meet at Nordell's and ask for his help in a delicate matter. The fact was, Runeberg owed Anckarström 200 riksdaler and could not pay up. Anckarström, he alleged, wanted to throw him into the debtor's gaol. Could Nordell see any way of avoiding such a disaster? But the district judge wanted no part of this business. He knew only too well how things stood between Anckarström and Runeberg. If Anckarström wanted to throw Runeberg in gaol for debt, it was simply because Runeberg was his wife's lover. No. Runeberg must get out of his quandary as best he could. Anyway, Anckarström would shortly have other things to think about, and was particularly busy this evening. Soon the lamps outside the Opera would be lighting up.

But at least Nordell would accept Runeberg's bankruptcy petition? No. He wouldn't do that either.

At long last the clerk Netzel turned up. He should really have been helping them to check the minutes. Nordell invited both him and Nystedt to come and have a bite to eat with him at York's Tavern, an English inn in the neighbourhood of the Sluice Bridges. Simple politeness required that he extend his invitation to the other two; but to his relief they declined. They were going somewhere else.

So Nordell, Netzel and Nystedt went off to York's Tavern. The host, Sundberg by name, found a table for them in the little red room, where there was only space for three diners. Neither Kajsa Örndahl, the fifteen-year-old girl, nor the seventeen-year-old waiter Gustaf Sander who together waited on them, knew who they were. Nor was the host particularly forthcoming. All he offered them to drink with their dinner was a bottle of small beer. Nor did the waitress recognize the little old gentleman with a skull-cap on his head, who suddenly appeared in the buttery and looked keenly about him. Seeing the tall man in the red room – Nordell – he entered hastily. It was Johan von Engeström. Nordell pulled up a chair and invited him to join them. But he had no time. He was to dine with one of his brothers. There were many brothers in the Engeström family, all gifted and respectable men; but most successful of all was Lars, the Swedish minister in Warsaw. Recently, among other touchy matters, he had become involved in Gustaf III's wild plans for getting himself elected King of Poland.

Nordell went out to have a private word with Johan:

'Pechlin has told me there'll certainly be a revolution tonight,' he whispered. 'The general wants me to go out and see what happens.'

Nordell instantly understood the euphemism. 'Go out and see what happens.'

'Then we'll go together. Come back here on your way home. I'll be waiting for you.'

After which Johan von Engeström went to his brother Lars, and Nordell returned to his two guests. After they had dined, they began playing *hombre*. Nordell, in a good humour now after what he had heard, became more lavish: ordered in a bottle of Moselle.

A goldsmith's apprentice, hanging about in Stora Vattugränd, beside swordmaker Damström's front door, heard someone come running down the dark alley. It was Horn. Finding the shutters of the swordsmith's shop barred and bolted, he swore aloud. And began banging on the door with his fists.

'I want my sabre!'

But Damström had already gone to bed. He was in poor health and this evening felt even worse than usual. All these hammerings infuriated him.

'Who's that?'

'The sabre was to be repaired by eight o'clock!' yelled Horn.

The swordsmith had not the least inclination to get out of bed for this aristocratic rowdy who hadn't made the effort to come back before closing time. And now it was nearly ten o'clock.

'You can fetch the sabre tomorrow, early, at half past five,' he shouted back in his squeaky voice, out of his bed.

'The devil I will! I want it now! I've got to leave town tomorrow before a soul's stirring. I've got to have it, I say!'

But no matter how Horn bawled and hammered, no reply came from within the shop. The goldsmith's apprentice, observing him curiously from the dark doorway, was just wondering what would be the upshot of this exchange of words when the count suddenly gave up and ran off down the narrow empty alley. His footsteps echoed among the walls of the houses.

Where should he get a sabre? If the mob should break loose after it had happened, he wouldn't stand much of a chance unless he had some such weapon about him. That damned swordsmith – that he hadn't had the gumption to open his door! Luckily, Horn happened to think of his friend Thure Funck. Funck usually had weapons in his house.

Like so many other 'patriots', Lieutenant Funck had resigned from the service at the beginning of the war against Russia. He lived in the Palinska House in Klara Södra Kyrkogata, next door to *Konsertmeister* Christian Freidrich Müller, husband of a pretty opera singer. Lights were shining from his window, and from the steps outside Horn could hear the delightful strains of a string orchestra. A Bach fugue – the one he himself had so often played in the days when he used to take lessons from Müller.

Tonight a dozen music-lovers had gathered here, either to play or to listen to what amateurs led by a professional could do. The concert had been arranged with the worthy aim of entertaining Johan Jakob De Geer from Finspång, a gentleman of the royal chamber. That was the nominal reason, at least. The curious circumstance that the musicians, like their guest of honour, all belonged to the opposition, was doubtless another matter. Funck was one of the players.

Reluctant to show himself, Horn had a servant summon Funck out into the lobby.

A sabre? A trivial service, to be sure, on such an evening. As it happened his big service sabre was propped up in Müller's room, behind the drawing room where the violinists were sawing away. Just as the last bars of the fugue came to an end they were suprised to see him carry it out into the lobby. Funck came back immediately. His face wreathed in smiles, he skipped about and swung his legs like a ballet dancer. In a perfect French accent he sang:

'*Victoire*! *Victoire*!'

His servant, Ludvig Kruus, who was helping Müller's servants to lay the supper table, understood *that* much French, at least. He was not particularly fond of his master. Seeing him make such a fool of himself, he only scorned him all the more.

Anckarström was lying with outstretched legs in his room. He had had supper, and was just dropping off to sleep when someone woke him by banging on his door. It was Horn. Under his long overcoat he was wearing Funck's sabre. Unbelting it, he stood it in a corner.

'I've had to walk miles because of that damned Damström!' he swore. 'As if moving to Vattugränden wasn't enough, the only sabre he had that was any good had to be repaired. And when I came to fetch it, the damned blockhead had turned in.'

'Oh, and where did you get that one from, then?' Anckarstöm inquired.

'Funck lent it to me.'

Horn was a bundle of nerves. Did not even give himself time to sit down.

Anckarström's diamond-studded watch was lying on the table. 'Ten,' he said, casting a glance at it. 'In an hour from now I'll be back here to change. That'll be time enough.'

Horn vanished as quickly as he had come. He must be going to his sister's-in-law, thought Anckarström to himself. The Misses Linnerhjelm, too, had promised to come to the masquerade. Going over to his desk, he took out the two demi-pistols, powder and shot, and anything else he could find to stuff down their barrels. After loading them, he glued some black taffeta on to the kitchen knife. A white handle would be too conspicuous.

It was just about then that Petter Bark, a cakemaker's apprentice, was walking along the street in the direction of Norrmalmstorg, the big square outside the Opera, carrying a basket. The basket contained a coffee pot, wrapped in a woollen shawl. His master – cakemaker Sundberg – was the lessee of one of the sweet stalls on the square, and the girl who attended it had to have something warm to drink. Having delivered his basket, Petter had no desire to go straight home again. For by now the lamps in front of the Opera had been lit, the Royal Suite behind the façade, too, was a flood of light, and inside the vestibule Petter Bark caught glimpses of liveried lackeys and soldiers of the Second Life Guards. Here came a couple of musicians, with their instruments in their cases. The boy was curious to see what the fancy-dresses and the masks would look like. But so far none had arrived. It was still only ten. A few other youngsters, equally curious, clustered around him.

Only a few feet away, Lieutenant-Colonel Lilliehorn was standing observing them. He had been trying to make up his mind which boy to approach. Petter Bark looked both simple-minded and honest.

'Do you know Rémy, the king's servant?' Lilliehorn asked

him in a low voice.

Petter gazed up at the tall gentleman in the blue overcoat. Sometimes his master had sent him on errands up to the Palace, so he did not hesitate. Yes! Of course he knew Rémy.

'Then will you do me the service of giving him this letter? You'll get two *riksdalers* when you've done it.'

It was a lavish sum for so quickly executed an errand; so Petter Bark accepted. Disappearing inside the huge vestibule, he bounded up the stairs to the Royal Suite two steps at a time. The doors to the Hall of the Bodyguard stood open. Inside, lackeys were busy laying the supper table. Not seeing the man he was looking for, Petter turned to a footman who was just coming in with a pair of silver candelabra.

'Rémy? I saw him just a moment ago, on his way to the corner cabinet. What's it all about?'

'I'm to hand him this letter.'

At that moment a page called Aminoff came by. Seeing the letter was addressed to the king, he gave it to the footman.

'He shall get it,' said Aminoff.

For a while Petter Bark hung about; but when Rémy did not appear to give him his *riksdalers*, he felt he'd been fooled and ran off down the stone staircase. In the vestibule he saw that the man for whom he had run this errand had also vanished. Nor could he see any sign of him out in the square.

Outside the house where Lilliehorn lived Private Smith, soldier No.21 in the First Life Guards, began doing sentry-duty at ten o'clock. He, too, noticed the blue overcoat. Now it was visible in the lamplight in front of the façade of the Opera House, now swallowed up in the darkness over by the Slaughterhouse Bridge. As far as he could see, the Lieutenant-Colonel did not talk to anyone. A great many people seemed to be aimlessly straying about the streets. One or another had a lantern in his hand. Others managed to do without one, though they had to take care where they were putting their feet – the snow which had melted in the sunshine during the day had frozen hard again. The snow crackled under the soles of their boots. At the appointed time, Notary Enhörning fetched Councillor Alegren at his lodgings. When they got to Thure Bielke's lodgings on Malmskillnadsgatan, a couple of blocks above Brunkebergstorg, they went up to him. Dressed only in his shirt, trousers and stockings, the baron was lying in bed. They told him they were on their way to the masquerade.

'And what,' the baron asked, 'are you going to do there?'

Taking a candle, he followed them out into the lobby. Now they went down to Norrmalmstorg and across the North Bridge and through Mynttorget Square up the steep narrow slope of Storkyrkobrinken, between the Great Church and the Palace. The Councillor was intending to hire a domino costume at Hatter Svanholm's shop. But the shutters were up. So they didn't trouble themselves further to get Alegren a domino. Instead, their footsteps took them over Lejonbacken and the Slaughterhouse Bridge, back to Norrmalmstorg and the Opera House.

'How about a bite to eat?' Enhörning suggested. 'At Hanberg's in the Daevelska House? Or in the Opera Cellar?'

Alegren did not feel like eating. It was shortly his intention to return to Bielke. But Enhörning decided to slip into the Opera Cellar and refresh himself. Afterwards, perhaps, he would buy a ticket, sit in some box, and watch the masquerade. Their ways parted.

VI

ARE PEOPLE ALLOWED TO SHOOT AT MASQUERADES?

The Opera House on whose stage other actors than those possessing the gift of song were now to perform was the proudest of all the king's creations. Its main façade, overlooking Norrmalmstorg, went in noble French classical style. Above the ground floor, with its arcade of rounded arches, rose four massive Corinthian pilasters; and high up on the pediment in the centre of the façade, under the Swedish coat of arms, could be read the proud words: GUSTAVUS III PATRIIS MUSIS – *Gustaf III to the Muses of the Fatherland*. From the square, three portals gave access to a fairly spacious vestibule, whence vaulted stone staircases led off in every direction: to the pit, to the amphitheatre, and to the circles of boxes. To the right, on the ground floor, was a guard-room with a lockup. From the smaller left-hand vestibule the monumental Royal Staircase led up to the first floor and there divided, leading to the Royal Box on the one hand and to the Royal Suite, on the other.

This suite, behind the columns of the façade, ran almost its entire length. It comprised, first, a large hall. The walls of this hall, known as Drabantsalen – the Hall of the Bodyguard – were panelled in off-white, with sculpted and gilded mouldings. It was sparsely furnished. In this room a table had been laid for supper.

Next to the Hall of the Bodyguard – in the direction of that end of the building which abutted on the Stream – was a drawing room. It had two open fireplaces of veined marble and its walls were clad in blue and white East Indian damask, *à l'arabesque*. Passing through this room, one reached a corner cabinet, with walls in yellow and crimson satin. There was one more room in the Royal Suite, but to reach it from the corner cabinet one had to pass through a little antechamber. Known as the Little Cabinet, its single window looked out over the Stream and the firewood ferries where they lay at the corner of the great quay of Skeppsbron, beneath the Palace. A pier-glass. A few chairs. A divan upholstered in red. Such were the only furnishings of the Little Cabinet. Here the king loved to retire. Here he could be in peace.

The Little Cabinet was directly connected with the stage by a narrow stairway built into its rear wall. The interior of the Opera was designed, in other words, in such a way that auditorium and stage did not run inwards from the façade on Norrmalmstorg back towards the park at the other side, but parallel with the façade, towards The Stream and the harbour.

At the appointed hour Horn turned up and fetched Anckarström. They changed their clothes and went to the square. Horn was as heavily armed as Anckarström: his pocket pistols were loaded with smallshot and he had brought his powder flask and a bag for shot. On the quay, where building work on the new North Bridge was going on, a mass of stones and timber beams lay heaped. With Anckarström's consent Horn took his sabre and hid it among the timber. Into a cavity he also stuffed his own two pocket pistols and the sabre he had borrowed from Funck. Now only Anckarström was armed. With a demi-pistol in his breast-pocket beneath his domino outfit and another in his fob. Also with the long knife, wrapped in black taffeta.

The masked ball was to begin at half-past ten, but those who were intending to go to it knew from experience that there was no need to turn up so early. The footman Peter Fagerberg, however, a mere looker-on, was there by about ten. He took up his position in the wings of the stage. After quite a long wait he saw a black domino come in. He was wearing a round hat and a white mask. After he had walked about alone awhile in the theatre where the masquerade was to take place, three other similarly attired masks came in and walking up and down with him talked to the first. From where he stood in the wings, Fagerberg saw five more masks join the first comers. If he paid them particular attention it was because of the curious circumstance of their all being dressed alike. He counted up to nine black dominoes, chatting together in a cluster.

Now, above their heads, the immense forty-branched crystal chandelier had been lit and men at the winch specially provided for the purpose were hoisting it up to a suitable height on its blue and yellow rope. The chandelier illumined the theatre with great brilliance, causing the white-lacquered panelling of the boxes to shine and all the gilded palms, acanthus leaves and festoons to gleam and glimmer. Looking up, as many as four tiers of boxes could be counted, each circle being somewhat less elaborately embellished than the one beneath it. Most splendid of all was the Royal Box, at the rear of the first circle. Actually it comprised three distinct boxes, each with its own grille.

Through the main entrance beneath the centre of the Royal Box some more masks came into the pit. Strolling up to the stage, they found their way via the left wings out into the foyer where Deland was serving coffee, tea and liqueurs. Now some of the musicians began to show up. They, too, had been ordered to dress in domino.

Now the guards arrived: the Royal Bodyguard, whose rank and file were lieutenants and in which a captain held the rank of corporal. But this evening the proceedings were to be under the surveillance of the Second Regiment of Life Guards, noted for their loyalty to the king. The soldiers began to take post at the entrances.

In front of the portals on the square one sledge after another came driving up and stopped, and polite gentlemen helped their ladies to alight. Here came Pierrots and Pierinas, califs and odalisques, pirates and slave-girls. Under such guises no distinction was being drawn tonight between blue blood and the commoner variety, and noblemen came driving up with women from the bourgeoisie. From the box of one hackney sledge Nisse Åberg jumped lightly down, as Strussenfelt and Plomgren helped Mamsell Regina to descend. Hans Hierta, however, stayed behind in the sledge and ordered the coachman to drive on out to Ladugårdslandet, where he was to fetch little Anna Johanna Unge. Here came the Misses Linnerhjelm, and the wife of Gjörwell the royal librarian, diarist and indefatigable writer for the newspapers. Exercising the prerogative of his sixty years, Gjörwell had himself preferred to stay at home and go on to bed.

What persons in high authority could be expected? The king, of course. Unquestionably. But he was still at the Bollhus Theatre, just beyond the palace, watching *Les Folies Amoureuses*. Crispin's role tonight was being played by Louis Deland, regarded as the best comic actor in Sweden, and the king had not wished to deny himself the pleasure of going to laugh at him. The queen was not to be counted on. But perhaps Duke Charles of Södermanland, the king's brother, would be coming in company with his young duchess and the king's sister? Rumour had it that the Duke had forbidden his spouse to attend the masquerade. And in fact he had sent word to his brother that he wasn't coming. He was too busy compiling a catalogue of his collection of books, and would soon retire to bed.

The clock in the tower of St James's Church, just behind the Opera House, had struck eleven when the royal party came driving over the Slaughterhouse Bridge. Curious night-strollers hurried over to catch a glimpse of the monarch before he had time to disappear into the temple of the muses. A few clambered up on to the pedestal of the equestrian statue of Gustavus Adolfus where, still shrouded in its drapery, it stood looming in the darkness.

With lively steps the king went up his fine wide staircase and entered the Hall of the Bodyguard, where a rousing fire crackled in the open fireplace and the candelabra on the supper table had just been lit by officious royal lackeys. He was wearing a grey jacket of shot silk stockinget and round his waist a broad sash of the same material. On the left side of his chest, by the row of buttons, he sported the embroidered star of the Order of the Seraphim and underneath it the smaller decoration of a knight of the grand cross of the Order of the Sword. His shirt had a lace collar and lace cuffs. Stockinget pantaloons clung tightly to his legs.

He went straight to table, with Baron Hans Henrik von Essen, the crown equerry, on his right, and his adjutant, Captain Löwenhielm, on his left. The rest of the party consisted of gentlemen of the chamber: De Besche, Möllersvärd, Borgenstierna and Captain Stiernblad. There were no others.

Formerly the Chief of Police, Liljensparre, had always been present at public spectacles and masquerades to maintain order. But the king, excusing Liljensparre from this duty, had transferred responsibility for the security arrangements to the military duty-officer. As it was the Second Life Guards who were on duty this evening, the responsibility fell on its second-in-command, General Armfelt. Normally, Armfelt would himself have made one of the royal party: but he had been invited to the Danish Minister, Count Reventlow, and was not present at supper. He had intended to take his leave before the Danish Minister's guests sat down to table, but out of consideration for that admirable man had stayed on.

At long last Armfelt found a suitable moment to leave. But as he did so he was detained by Baron von Düben, one of the auditors of the National Debt Office. To Armfelt's great annoyance the latter launched out into a long and tedious discussion of some matter to do with the audit and the conversation looked as though it was never going to end.

Armfelt longed to get away. Little did he guess that Düben, one of the aristocratic conspirators, was trying to detain him as long as he possibly could.

At last he broke away, and hurried off home to change into fancy dress.

As a tall figure in a blue overcoat swiftly approached the door of his house, Soldier No.21, Smith, jumped smartly to attention. Now he could see who it was. But instead of walking straight in, Lilliehorn turned to the sentry.

'You know me?' he asked curtly.

'Yes, lieutenant-colonel.'

'Have you a key to the door?'

'No, sir. But they'll let you in if you knock.'

The loud blows of the knocker were heard by the footman Krantz, who made haste to open the door. He asked whether he was to help his master take off his boots and undress, as usual. But tonight the lieutenant-colonel had no intention of going to bed. No sooner had he taken off his overcoat than he ordered Krantz to help him on with his wolfskin.

Soldier No.21, Smith, saw him come out again.

'Must be off to the Opera House now,' he supposed; but noticed that the lieutenant-colonel was not wearing fancy dress under his furs. Once again, he just walked to and fro on the square, taking care not to approach the illuminated façade too closely. Suddenly he came back and went up into the house. Yet no light went on at his window. Must have gone to bed after all, thought Smith; and to keep out the cold he began doing sentry-duty outside the door. The clock of the Great Church struck twice, echoed by the bell of St James's, just behind the Opera House.

Supper in the royal suite was nearly at an end when the page, Tigerstedt, handed the king a sealed letter.

'Who from?'

'A lackey of the royal chamber gave it to me. He said an

unknown man brought it up to him.'

The king broke the seal and read through the letter, twice. Out of decorum, Löwenhielm, on his left, averted his head, but the expression on the page's face urged him to cast a glance at the letter. It was written in pencil, in French; and bore no signature. The king stuffed it into his jacket pocket.

'Find out who brought it.'

The page went out, and the conversation turned to other things; so no one heard where the letter came from. When the meal was over, Löwenhielm wondered whether it was not time for them to be putting on their masks.

'Not yet,' said the king. 'But you can hurry on down to your little beauty.'

This, to Löwenhielm, was an order. After he, with ill-concealed eagerness, had left the room, the king took the anonymous letter out of his pocket and showed it to von Essen. The equerry was disturbed, indignant. Begged him not to go down into the theatre. The king just laughed – a hard, metallic laugh.

'Am I to let them think I'm afraid? Surely you know I've had many such letters before – yet nothing has ever happened?'

'No one imagines Your Majesty is afraid,' Essen objected.

The king stuffed the letter back into his pockets, beneath the waist-sash, and got up from table. Through a narrow passage he walked out to his little circular box in the first circle, with its grille: the *oeil de boeuf*. From here he could observe at close range everything that was happening on the stage. Essen placed himself beside him. The orchestra had not begun to play, and as yet no one was dancing. But over by the orchestra – this evening it had been placed on a balcony – a group of masks, all wearing black dominoes and round beaver hats, hurried downstage. Facing the Royal Box, they looked up at the king, as he stood there arm in arm with Essen.

Again Essen appealed to the king not to go down into the

theatre. At the very least he should allow his party to surround him, or else don a mail shirt under his jacket.

'Well, now they've had their chance to shoot. Come, let's go down.'

A long while the king had been standing there in his box, framed like a picture. Suddenly he drew the grille and returned to the Royal Suite.

On the stage Ribbing, standing beside Anckarström and Horn, had been staring up defiantly at the Royal Box. If there was anyone he hated, it was von Essen, the royal favourite. Von Essen had been responsible for the bitterest set-back of Ribbing's life . . .

It was only a few years since it happened. With all the violence characteristic of his tempestuous nature, Ribbing had fallen in love with Charlotte de Geer, who had responded to his feelings. Her father, the wealthy Baron de Geer, however, had been reluctant to marry off his daughter until she was twenty. This had led Ribbing to renew his courtship – only to hear that she had just become engaged to von Essen. Such an insult was more than he could tolerate. He had challenged his rival to a duel, and no one, not even his mother's lover Maclean, had been able to make him change his mind. He was going to kill, honourably, or else be killed. The duel had been fought in the *manège* of the royal stable on Holy Spirit Island, and all the orders and royal decorations on von Essen's breast had not sufficed to ward off Ribbing's rapier. Fastening in a rib just above the heart, the thrust had been so fierce that the rapier had snapped. The duel was over. But Essen, after lingering a long time between life and death, had recovered.

More quickly, indeed, than the wound in Ribbing's heart. The king, who had arranged von Essen's engagement to Charlotte de Geer, had been incensed. And Ribbing believed it was because of this duel that he had not been posted to Finland like all the other officers during the war, but with his troops had been sent to reinforce the garrison of the god-forsaken fortress of Waxholm, commanding the entrance to the inner archipelago. Whereon, his feelings hurt and his pride outraged, he had quit the service and withdrawn to his mother's estate at Sjöholm.

In the little cabinet, Elfström, the footman, had laid out several fancy dresses. The king came in, followed by von Essen, and thoughtfully tried to choose between them; but none seemed quite to his taste. Several times he sent the footman out for others. In the theatre the band could now be heard playing a minuet.

In the end Gustaf settled on a Venetian cape of black taffeta, but slung it so loosely over his shoulder that the embroidered order of the Seraphim was still clearly visible on his jacket. As if overcoming some inner reluctance, he put on a black beaver hat, adorned with white plumes. The white mask was sewn on to it.

They went down the little stair to the stage. Taking Essen, now also masked, by his left arm, Gustaf III began walking with quick steps towards his great box. De Besche hurried after him, keeping close to his right side. On the stone bench by the wall under one of the two *oeils de boeuf* Löwenhielm was sitting with his pretty lady. Coming up to them with his attendants, the king halted:

'May the lovely mask be gracious to her swain,' he said with an elegant turn of phrase. 'A moment ago, for her sake, he was in a great hurry to leave me.'

The king continued his promenade. Having walked once right round the theatre and begun a second circumambulation, he went between the wings on the left side of the stage and mounted the little stairs leading to the artistes' lounge, where Deland was serving refreshments.

Both from the white plumes in his beaver hat and from the order glimpsed under the domino, Ribbing had no difficulty in recognizing him. He gave a sign for the conspirators to gather. Kurck, Horn, Hierta, Plomgren, Strussenfelt and many others followed him, pressing close to the wings beyond which the king had made his exit. Behind them the masked company was dancing a quadrille. The king had left the stage. All they needed now was to wait until he came back the same way, to make his last entry onto the stage which is the world. At any moment they might expect him.

Up in the orchestra a few feet away the court trumpeter Örnberg was astonished to see so many identically clad masks flocking together. Fifteen, sixteen dominoes he counted. He fancied it must be the Opera troupe with whom, the previous evening, he rehearsed some dances and who, he now supposed, were going to perform on the stage. But Kluth, the leader of the orchestra, paid them no attention. Just went on beating time with his baton.

Country dances – *contradances* – were all the rage. In the closed square formed by the dancers the *première* side had made their turns and now these were being repeated by the ranks of the *seconde*. Next time the gay tune in the major was repeated, the complicated turns of the *contradance* would place greater demands on the dancers' ability to remember the right steps to the melody.

Baron Hierta had invited little Mamsell Unge to dance this quadrille with him, but she declined because of the great crush. Now she was standing with her partner near the wings where the men in black were clustering, and right beside her she recognized Plomgren and Strussenfelt, with Mamsell Regina. It was a quarter to twelve.

The crush was terrific; not only on stage but also in the narrow space between the wings and the actors' foyer. On the stairs leading up to the actors' foyer some servants who had nothing better to do sat down and as the king, still accompanied by von Essen, came back, the guards on duty there were obliged to shove them aside with their muskets. On the stairs the king met his adjutant, Captain Carl Fredrik Pollet. Pollet was just off home, and was looking for his servant in the crowd.

The king saluted him graciously, asked after his father. Had he heard anything from him? As they were speaking, the king and von Essen, with Pollet behind them, went on walking towards the wings. The music played. The dance was in full swing. The crowd, growing ever denser, brought them to a standstill. With his free right hand, then, Essen, without letting go of the king – who was gripping Essen's left arm – tried to clear a passage. As for Pollet, he had been thrust back by the press. At last they could begin moving again. They entered the stage and followed the wings down towards the *oeil de boeuf*. Now they had reached the first pair of wings, only four or five feet from the auditorium.

Anckarström, standing in the wings, had been watching the king move towards the left. He moved into position, as close as possible behind him. In his left hand he was holding the knife, wrapped in its black taffeta. Swiftly, from his breast pocket under his domino, he took out one of his pistols. It was ready cocked. Bending down, he pressed the weapon against the king's back. But at that instant the king, intending to say something to Pollet, turned to his left. The unexpected movement surprised the assassin, shook his nerve. His hand fell. No longer was he aiming at the heart. But at the midriff.

The pistol went off. The king gave a start.

'*Ay ay, je suis blessé!*'

Clasping his thigh, he gripped Essen's shoulder. The equerry, confused, went on trying to force a path to help the king over to the stone seat under the *oeil de boeuf*. The king ripped off his mask.

'Fire! Fire!' shouted all the men in black. Their cries were taken up in various quarters of the theatre – but failed to cause the expected panic. Someone stamped with his boots and clapped his hands. But the orchestra just went on playing, and the dancers were still weaving to and fro in the involved movements of the quadrille. Confounded not to see the king fall, Anckarström let the discharged pistol slip down his thigh to the stage floor, dropped the knife, and rushed away, trying to force his way through the crowd out of the auditorium, and so flee by the main exit under the Royal Box.

'Close the doors!' thundered the tall Pollet in a stentorian voice; and drawing his sabre himself hastened to one of the exits. Fancying someone had thrown a squib, Löwenhielm, who had been standing close by, leaped forward.

'What's happened?'

'Some wretch has shot the king,' shouted Essen.

Löwenhielm drew his rapier, driving back those masks who had not yet had time to put themselves at a safe distance.

'*Arrêtez-le mais ne lui faites de mal!*' the king called out after him.

Many others besides Löwenhielm misunderstood what had happened. At ten or twelve paces from the place of the crime one officer, Captain Engelbrekt, turned to Captain Stiernblad:

'What – are people allowed to shoot at masquerades?'

'Oh, it was just a squib,' Stierblad replied, unconcerned.

A major, standing in the king's great box, thought the same. And a schoolmaster near a door to the pit did not know whether the shot had come from within the theatre or outside.

In the gloom of the vestibule Nisse Åberg had been sitting on a bench as he waited to follow Mamsell Regina and her company home. He was jerked out of his slumbers by the tramp of boots and resounding cries:

'Fire! Fire!'

Capes flying, a score of men were rushing for the exit. Scared, the eleven-year-old forgot all about his instructions to wait, and ran out into the square. Behind him the doors were slammed shut by implacable guards. Shrieking women and their embittered partners found themselves being driven back by drawn sabres.

Some of the conspirators had succeeded in escaping. But

for most all retreat was cut off. Ehrensvärd, the man who had been chosen to bear the tidings of the king's death, resigned himself. What purpose, anyway, was to be served now by getting away – with no death to announce?

The king's jacket had been blackened and scorched by powder-smoke and Essen had to quench the glowing cloth. For a brief moment the king fainted away, but soon came to. Although blood was oozing from the wound, he felt no great pain. His only wish was to get back to the cabinet.

'*Je me sens faible. Conduisez-moi dans mes appartements*'.

Supported by von Essen, he got up from the stone seat. Löwenhielm supported him on the other side, and together they led him across the stage and up the stairs at its rear. In the cabinet he lay down on the red-covered divan.

Frightened out of his wits, Nisse Åberg was rushing away through the darkness along the quay where the waters of the Stream swirled blackly. Again and again he turned to see if flames were leaping against the night sky. But no signs of a fire were to be descried. Nor was any church bell sounding the three strokes which always meant that a fire had broken out on the north side of the city. Nor were any warning shots being fired from the cannon on Skeppsholmen Island, in the middle of the harbour. Reaching the general's house, he breathlessly rang the doorbell. Lönngren opened.

'Fire! Fire!' gasped the boy.

'Where?'

'At the Opera! They was shoutin' out 'twas on fire and runnin' out into the square!'

'What nonsense, boy!'

'And then they yelled that the guards was to shut the doors and not let no one out!'

The great door of Pechlin's house was slammed shut by Lönngren. The general who, clad in his dressing gown and sucking at his pipe, had been stumping about up in the drawing room, heard the boy's shrill voice down in the vestibule.

Half-opening the door, he listened to what was being said. Fire! The agreed signal! The shout that was to throw everything into confusion! So – the deed was done. The murderer had fired his shot. But – why close the doors? And why wasn't Pontus Lilliehorn ordering the drums to sound the *générale*?

He called the boy, began cross-examining him; but realizing he would get no coherent replies, sent the lad off to bed. The general ordered Lönngren to keep a lively watch at the front door until Miss Pettersson and her company were safely home. He was to admit no one who wouldn't give his name. After which, locking the drawing-room door, Pechlin retired into his bedroom.

From his apartment, plunged in darkness, Lilliehorn had seen the masked men come rushing out and fling themselves into hired sledges, the doors of the Opera House being closed, and pages and lackeys darting hither and thither in the Royal Suite. From all of which he concluded that the tragedy which, at the last moment, he had tried to avert, had nevertheless occurred. Now the whole fateful decision lay with him. Why hadn't Ehrensvärd brought the message? What could be detaining him?

Lilliehorn could wait no longer. Putting on his blue overcoat, he ran downstairs. Outside the house he saw to his satisfaction that the sentry had been relieved – his successor would have no call to wonder why the lieutenant-colonel, after coming in only half an hour ago in his wolfskin, should now be on his way out again dressed quite differently. Crossing the square, Lilliehorn was informed by one of the guards outside the closed doors of the Opera House that the king had been wounded.

Perhaps it was still not too late to sound the *générale*? Perhaps the royalists would still not have time to put up an organized resistance before the First Life Guards and the artillery and the citizen volunteers could strike? But with the army's supreme commander still alive, in whose name was the order to be given? Perhaps the only result would be bloody skirmishes, even a civil war, of uncertain outcome?

Lilliehorn stood paralysed. To make such a decision, all on his own, was too much for him. He felt a need to consult cooler heads than his own. Unseen in the darkness, he hastened over to General Pechlin's house and rang the doorbell. This awakened the curiosity of Mrs Sundström, one of two servants who were scrubbing the floors inside. Taking her candle, she went out to the lobby to see what was up. Lönngren had opened the door. Outside, hiding his face in its collar, stood a tall slim man in a blue overcoat. She heard the footman say the baron had gone to bed; but the visitor, ignoring him, dashed upstairs and tried to get into the drawing room. Mrs Sundström could hear him hammering at the door and tugging at the door-knob. Then he came dashing down again, and, still hiding his face in his collar, disappeared through the doorway without answering Lönngren's sullen question who he was.

Mrs Sundström went back to the sitting room, where Inga Jönsdotter, on all fours, was wiping the floor with a rag.

Blood, oozing from the wound, was staining both the jacket and the cover of the divan. The shot, it seemed, had not gone very deep, for Gustaf neither groaned nor complained. Among all the terrified lackeys and jittery pages he alone kept his head, giving orders in a calm controlled voice. Despatched Casimir Reuterskiöld to inform the Duke of what had befallen. Sent subalterns to alert the Chancellor, the Adjutant-General and other high officials, and to fetch a doctor. Also, of course, Liljensparre, the Chief of Police.

Löwenhielm was ordered to go down into the theatre and find out what was going on. To his amazement he found the orchestra still playing and people dancing. As yet not everyone had realized what had occurred. On his own initiative Löwenhielm sent the alarm to the Light Dragoons in their quarters at the Tiltyard, ordering them to man the customs barriers and make sure no one left the city.

When the order to take off all masks was given, the men in black began by refusing; but presently commonsense told them that to continue doing so would only draw suspicion on themselves, and they complied. As Löwenhielm was walking about the auditorium he ran into Ribbing and Kurck. They asked how things were with the king, and he gave them a calming answer.

'God be thanked!' said Ribbing. 'If only they catch the scoundrel!'

The diplomatic corps were not in the habit of absenting themselves from masked balls. Hurrying upstairs, the Prussian, Spanish and Russian ministers demanded an audience to express their solicitude. They were amazed at the king's courage, his presence of mind.

'Sire,' expostulated the Prussian minister, Stackelberg, mildly reproachful. 'In spite of the warning!'

'Thank you, count,' said the king, 'but when one madman wants to give his life for another's in the end he is always successful.'

In the pit the masquerade guests were standing in groups, talking. Harlequins and pierrettes, shepherds and their shepherdesses. A peasant in homespun turned out to be none other than Abraham Westman, the royalist brewer. A major, his cheeks blushing scarlet, was demanding permission to send his servant home to fetch his uniform – he had just arrived at the ball, dressed as a woman, and was furious to find himself cutting such a ridiculous figure.

'What wouldn't I give for a dram!' he exclaimed with a sigh. Neither Horn nor Ribbing spoke to Anckarström who had failed to make his getaway but had not yet been identified as the assassin. They pretended not to know him.

At all the exits guards officers and subalterns stood with drawn sabres. They had taken all the keys out of the locks and put them in their pockets.

'Did you see who fired the shot?'

Anckarström put the question to the court trumpeter Örnberg who after changing into his ordinary overcoat had left the bandstand and gone down into the theatre.

'Yes,' replied Örnberg.

'Let's hope they catch him,' mumbled Anckarström, simulating indignation.

'Haven't I the honour of knowing you, sir?'

'I'm a captain.' Anckarström did not give his name.

'Well, then, may I offer you a glass of punch?' enquired the court trumpeter.

Together they went between the wings up to Deland's coffee-room, where a huge crowd of the thirsty had conglomerated. The offer calmed Anckarström; as yet no one seemed to suspect him. But when the glass was set before him he lost all taste for punch.

'I've changed my mind,' he said curtly. 'I'm not drinking.'

Disappointed, the court trumpeter pouted: but thought to himself – not so surprising, after all. Everyone was indignant at the dastardly act. After Örnberg had taken a sip, they both went back to the theatre. Suddenly Anckarström took out a *riksdaler* and offered it to Örnberg. The latter protested vehemently: the drink had been on him. But Anckarström insisted, tried to force the coin on him. Örnberg's refusal to accept the *riksdaler* impressed Anckarström. An honest man, obviously.

'You're a good fellow,' he said. 'May I have a word with you in private?'

'Isn't here good enough?'

Anckarström looked about him. And in fact they were more or less alone. He asked:

'Do you know if the king was badly hurt?'

'Yes.'

'How do you know?'

'I heard it from a footman who'd just come down from the

king's room.'

'What did he look like, the one who fired the shot?'

The court trumpeter let his gaze travel over the nearest masks, as if looking for someone resembling the assassin. Then turned it on the captain:

'He was about as tall as yourself, and dressed like you.'

Anckarström, pretending to catch sight of an acquaintance in that garish assembly, bowed curtly and walked away.

Half the front door was opened to admit General Armfelt. Stepping into the vestibule, he looked round. Everything was perfectly in order, it seemed. As second-in-command of the Second Life-Guards he was responsible for his subalterns' behaviour. That these magnificent lads, not of noble birth perhaps, yet always attentive to their duties, should be looked down on by the young blue-blooded coxcombs of the Blue-and-Yellow, was more than he could stand. Armfelt was so deeply absorbed in inspecting his men that he noticed nothing amiss in his surroundings.

Making to cross the pit and stage to go up to the king's room, he found himself stopped at the doors by a sentry.

'You've the right to go in, General; but not to come out again.'

Armfelt flew into a rage. What, was the fellow out of his mind? How dare he prevent a man of his standing from coming and going as he pleased? Armfelt grabbed the door-knob. The sentry took a step towards him:

'The king has been wounded by a pistol shot, sir, and no one is allowed out. They're trying to arrest the assassin.'

The general refused to believe him. Confused, he turned back, meaning to enter by some other door. But suddenly after a few paces, his strength failed him, his knees seemed to be giving way. He began to mount the royal staircase. In the vestibule not a soul was in sight. The dining room was illumined only by a single burnt-down candle. Beside the tiled stove sat a little page, in tears.

'Where's the king?'

'In the divan, sir,' the boy sobbed.

'Wounded?'

'Yes.'

Armfelt's strength returned. He rushed through the drawing room and the corner cabinet, where only a few footmen were standing. An unusual silence reigned in all the rooms.

In the doorway to the little cabinet Armfelt thrust his way past some pages and lackeys. The Spanish and Prussian ministers were still there. Seeing his favourite, the king exclaimed:

'My friend, could you ever have imagined I'd be wounded in the back?'

Seeing how upset Armfelt was, he smiled and held out his hand:

'No need to be so terrified, my dear Armfelt. *You* know what it's like to be wounded. This is nothing. It doesn't even hurt.'

But Armfelt saw that the grey mantle swathing the lower part of the king's body was soaked in blood. He was so upset he could only stammer out a few words. Again, ill and weak as he still was after his severe war-wounds, his strength failed him. The king invited him to be seated. The Spanish minister, Chevalier Corral, brought him a glass of water. Armfelt asked whether they'd sent for Théel or Acrel, the royal physicians. Taking his hand, the king whispered in his ear:

'Send someone to see if La Perrière's at home. I thought I saw him standing near me.'

Armfelt did as he was bid. That the king should suspect La Perrière didn't surprise him in the least. An actor in the French company, La Perrière was rather a poor one at that, who mostly had to content himself with old men's roles; but so much the fiercer Jacobin. The king's plans for a crusade against his fatherland, newly freed from tyrants, might well have driven him to the desperate deed.

Casimir Reuterskiöld had only come to the masquerade for his own pleasure. He had no duties to perform. But this did not excuse him from the painful errand of informing the Duke of the attempt on his brother's life. The Duke had, in fact, gone to bed.

'His Majesty . . . isn't very well . . . ' Reuterskiöld stammered out breathlessly.

'So he's worn his arms and legs off at last, has he?' muttered the Duke. 'I've long been expecting some such misfortune – the way he rushes about.'

'Sir, the king has been shot!'

'Shot?'

The Duke tumbled out of bed. Grabbed his clothes.

Johan von Engeström, who had promised to inform Pechlin as soon as anything occurred, was wandering about the streets. Walking down Arsenalsgaten (today's Hamngatan) from Blasieholmen, towards Norrmalmstorg and the Opera House, he fell in with Nordell and Netzel. Arriving together at the nearby Opera House, a few yards further on, they could see lights burning in the Royal Suite. A few minutes later a man came rushing out, flung himself into a sledge and yelled to the coachman to drive like the devil.

What was going on? Someone said the man was going to fetch Olof af Acrel, the king's doctor. Suspecting things were not quite going according to plan, Engeström and Nordell hung about on the scene of action. Walking westwards along Fredsgatan, they rounded Rosenbad and then came back again along the street flanking the Stream, and so returned to the square. Again and again they made their circuit of this block. From time to time a sleigh came flying up and stopped dead outside the Opera. Out of one stepped Wachtmeister, the Lord Chancellor. Out of another, Adjutant-General Klingspor. And who was this, casting anxious glances about him. It was Duke Charles. And who was this man who came driving in from Ladugårdslandet, a subaltern seated at his side?

Ah, this must be the Chief of Police. So the net was being drawn tighter round the prisoners inside the Opera House. Imperturbable, Liljensparre stepped quietly into the darkness of the Opera vestibule. And Engeström, Nordell and Netzel resumed their eternal circumambulations. Though they said nothing they had plenty of food for thought.

All of a sudden Liljensparre was standing there in the middle of the pit. He had paid a hasty visit to the king and received his verbal orders to find the assassin. So now all he had to do was to set about his difficult task. Already he was pretty well informed about the course of events. Hasselström, the subaltern, had time to tell him all about it on their way into town. And already the murder weapon had been found.

Liljensparre, standing there, surveyed it with expert eye. A demi-pistol of the more elegant sort, with a walnut butt and a charming rocco design. Inside its case, the manufacturer's name: Wåhlberg, Stockholm. A name not unknown to the Chief of Police.

The knife, too, was handed to him by Adjutant Oldenburg. He had found it on the floor and put it into his pocket. It was so sharp that although it had only been inside his pocket a short while it had cut his coat to ribbons. The Chief of Police nodded. Thank God the assassin hadn't used it as well!

Liljensparre was just about to begin his interrogations – Örnberg, the trumpeter, and Fagerberg, the servant, had already said they could volunteer a great deal of information – when a second pistol was handed in. Exactly like the other, it was the work of the same gunsmith. And still loaded.

'I found it over there, by the Queen's Box.'

The person who found it pointed out the spot. Liljensparre frowned. A score of masks had had time to escape before the doors were closed. And now – this pistol, found only a few feet from the main exit. Thrown away, certainly by the fleeing assassin. This boded no good. The king suspected La

Perrière. But already the man sent by Armfelt to get news of him had come back and reported that the actor and his wife had all the time been fast asleep in their conjugal bed.

Liljensparre clapped his hands. The murmur of voices died away.

He ordered everyone to assemble on the stage. The women in their gay colourful clothes and the men in their strange fantastic outfits or – for the most part – grey or black dominoes, obeyed. Guards with fixed bayonets made sure that no one hid. Liljensparre had a table and a couple of chairs put out in the pit near the main exit, and a policeman brought writing materials. One by one the masqueraders came up to him. Politely, Liljensparre asked each how he or she was. Even went so far as to shake hands. No mere act of politeness, this. A firm handshake dispelled suspicion. A trembling one might say more than words. Name and address were noted down on the list.

While the mesh was being drawn tighter at the masquerade, Enhörning was thanking his lucky stars he hadn't walked into the wasp's nest. At the Opera Cellar, before the rumour of the terrible event reached him, he had had time for a drink, a sandwich and a bottle of lemonade. Other officials from the magistrature were also seated at his table – 'volunteers', Pechlin would have called them. They, too, had known very well what was going forward. And now – this gloomy news. The assassination had failed. Well, what now?

Magistrate Alegren told him he ought to go and inform Baron Bielke. Enhörning made haste to do so.

'Now we're in trouble!' he said.

In Bielke's temporarily hired room on Malmskilnadsgatan the servant Johan lay sleeping in a corner that had been partitioned off with chairs and clothing. This evening he had been told to go to bed. No need to help the baron undress. Now he was awakened by the creaking of the door and saw the baron standing there, candle in hand, whispering with a couple of gentlemen. But could not catch the words.

Bielke showed Enhörning out. And immediately afterwards Alegren, the city notary, also left and went straight home. Wilhelm Leuhusen, on a brief visit to his ex-tutor, had been sharing his room. He sat up in bed.

'The king was only wounded,' Enhörning said. 'There'll be no revolution tonight.'

All who stood around the king were amazed at his fortitude. First of many doctors to arrive was the court surgeon, Hallman. He was out of breath from running up the stairs.

'Look at my fat Hallman – he's gasping for breath!' said the king, laughing.

But when Hallman, after a thorough examination of the wound, could not say how serious it was, the laughter died on Gustaf's lips, turned to displeasure. Other doctors arrived. Elias Salomon. And Olof af Acrel. At last, after the wound had been bandaged, it was decided that the king should be moved to the Palace.

Gustaf III was not naturally a brave man. All his life he had had a congenital terror – of trifles. But at moments calling for courage and firmness, he always rose to the occasion, a man of infinite superiority, charm and ease of manner. He did not feel too ill to walk, he declared. But his doctor and courtiers overruled him. In a cradle draped with fur he was carried downstairs.

Outside in the square night-jays flocked around the king's covered carriage. By the time Engeström, Nordell and Netzel got there it was already in motion. Bodyguards were walking on either side.

'Whatever has happened?' asked Engeström, from where he stood near the statue of the hero-king. Of course, he knew very well. But sensing how embittered the atmosphere all round him was, feigned ignorance.

'The king's ill,' a stable hand told him.

At a slow trot, followed by a great swarm of people and with Armfelt and Essen sitting on either side of the king, the cavalcade passed over the Slaughterhouse Bridge. Gustaf suffered greatly from the jolting of the carriage, but as they reached the foot of the great flight of steps where they were once more to start carrying him, his expression changed. He thanked everyone for their kindness, and, in his usual friendly way and with all the charm he so well knew how to exploit whenever it was a question of exciting sympathy and enthusiasm for his own person, spoke to all who came near him.

'I'm like the Holy Father,' he joked. 'Carried in procession!'

That the wounded man, more than anything else, was in need of rest, seemed to occur to no one. Over the stone paving of the great interior courtyard of the Palace the crowd trampled in. Not even halting in the arched gateway, it went on up the stairs and even into the State Bedchamber. It was here – though he had not slept in it since his royal nuptials – Gustaf III wished to be laid. People off the streets mingled with courtiers, with officers and diplomats. The wounded monarch was undressed and put to bed almost in public. And the groom of the stole waited on him almost as if all this were no more than some great ceremonial occasion.

To write down all the names and addresses of the masquerade guests was a lengthy task. Liljensparre and his assistants were meticulousness itself. Everything was being done in the greatest detail and with maximum officiousness. No vagueness or carelessness was tolerated. Liljensparre's deliberate way of doing things was more than Claes Horn could stand. Going up to Adjutant-General Klingspor he asked to be allowed to leave the theatre at once. His wife, he lied, was lying ill at home out at Huvudsta. Klingspor's heart was not so hard he could not make an exception – seeing as how the countess was unwell.

Horn ran down the steps and out into the square. Unseen by the guards and the crowd of the curious still hanging about outside, he made for the heap of stones and timbers. Taking out the two pocket pistols from their hiding place, he threw them into the swirling waters of the Stream. Anckarström's sabre met the same fate. But round his waist Horn fastened the sabre he had borrowed from his friend Funck. He had no overcoat. It had been left behind at Anckarström's.

Going to the cab office, he ordered a hackney cab, and, while waiting for it to be got ready, hurried over to his father's stables near Klara Södra Kyrkogatan, intending to fetch his wolfskin. But his servant, who should have opened the door to him, was asleep in the tack room and didn't wake up. Afraid of making too much noise, Horn returned to the cab office and there got into the one he had ordered. The coachman was surprised at his light attire in the cold March night.

'I can't find my lackey,' said Horn. And drove out of town to Huvudsta. No one stopped him at the Karlberg barrier.

Three men were standing in Arsenalsgatan, behind the Opera, talking excitedly. This was the trio who had so long been keeping each other company: Johan von Engeström, Nordell and Netzel. Nordell was insisting that they inform Pechlin; but since Engeström knew him best, it was for him to do so. At last Engeström reluctantly gave in. The others watched him as he went up to the door. He rang the bell and there was a glimpse in the open doorway of someone with a lantern in his hand. Engeström came back.

'The servant won't let me in unless I tell him who I am.'

Nordell was angry. Well, and why shouldn't he give his name? In low voices they began squabbling. Engeström was in a tight spot, but suddenly saw a way out. A posse of the fire-watch were approaching. He asked the other two to stand

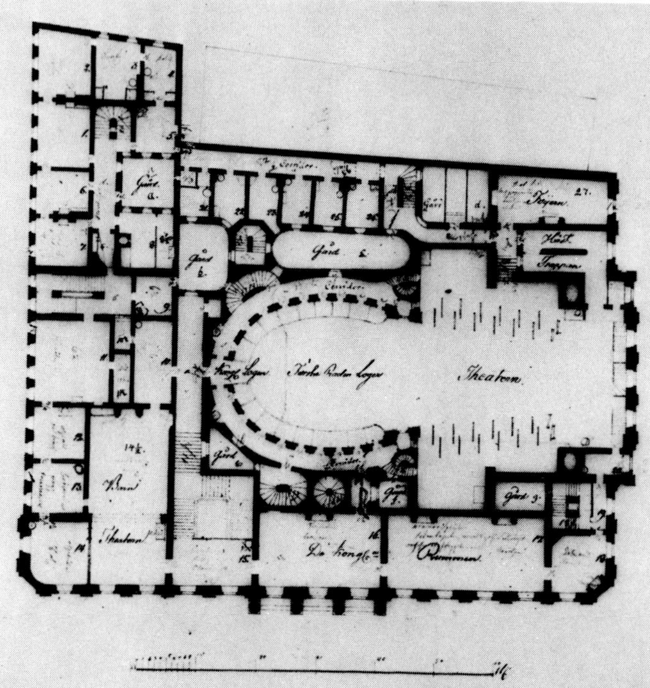

External view and plan of Gustaf III's Opera House (later burnt down and replaced by the present building).

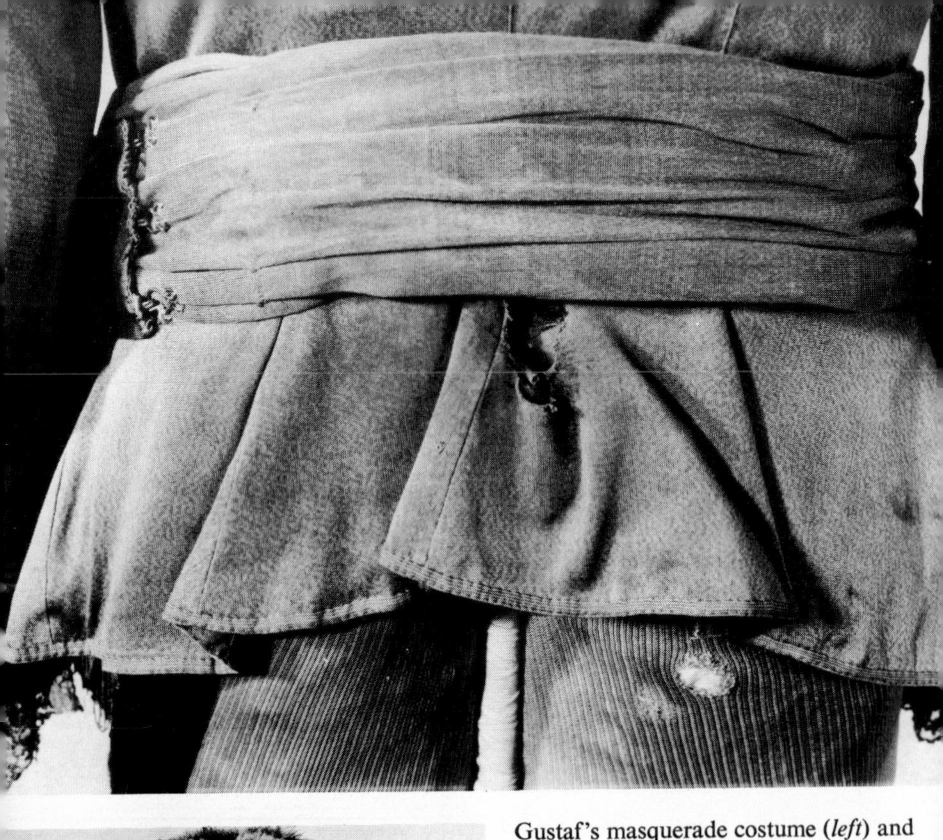

Gustaf's masquerade costume (*left*) and (*above*) a detail showing the hole made by the shot just below the sash.

aside. As soon as the watch had passed, he said, he would go up to the door again.

Nordell and Netzel consented. Hardly had Engeström seen them disappear round the corner of the house than, half-running and hidden by some low shanties, he managed to reach the Slaughterhouse Bridge by another route. At a smart pace he went straight off home to his house on the south side of the city. It was now the small hours of the night, and Engeström's servant was not used to seeing his master come home so late. Engeström said he had been detained by a game of cards.

In the theatre only a dozen names still remained to be noted down. Now a short man with sharp features was standing in front of the table.

'Surely you don't suspect me?'

'No, of course not.'

Liljensparre shrugged his shoulders. Many had asked him the same or similar questions hoping to convince him, of course, of their innocence. He put out his hand, asked mechanically how the other was. His name?

'Captain Jakob Johan Anckarström.'

The policeman took down his address. Now the next in turn was standing before the table. Shortly afterwards all the doors were thrown open.

Once again during that sleepless night Lönngren, Pechlin's servant, was awakened by the jangling of the front door bell. Was he never to get any rest? First there had been that tall fellow in the blue overcoat. Forcing his way in past him, he'd hammered on the drawing-room door and then vanished again into the night. Afterwards, other strange figures had come and woken him up, and gone off again without leaving their names. One who, he thought, resembled Engeström, had been equally anxious, equally reticent. And then there had been another, asking whether some court secretary or other was with the general. Once again Lönngren sullenly unlocked the door. This time, however, he gave a sigh of relief. At last!

In her long dress, her fur collar so loosely flung about her shoulders that her white bobbing bosom was quite exposed, Mamsell Regina Pettersson came rustling in. Strussenfelt was holding her round the waist. After them came Hierta, with little Miss Unge. She was so tired that she tottered on the steps. When ensign Plomgren, too, had come in, Lönngren turned the great key in the lock.

The mamsell went up and knocked on the general's bedroom door. He had been lying there awake, waiting. Now he got up and let her in. Sitting down on the edge of his bed, she began to tell him everything that had happened. He had every confidence in her reliability as a witness; but she was so exhausted that her replies to his questions were all jumbled up and disjointed. After a while Pechlin sent her out to boil some water for his tea and, one by one, called in the others to gain as clear a picture as possible.

Pale, tired to death, Anna Johanna Unge sat in the anteroom, looking out over the silent city. Servants were lighting their masters home along Skeppsbron Quay, and their little bobbing yellow lanterns seemed to her like will-o'-the-wisps. Behind her, Strussenfelt and Plomgren walked to and fro. They were too nervous even to sit down.

'We're going to hear a lot of nasty things after this,' said Strussenfelt.

By the time Liljensparre had let all the masqueraders out of the theatre it was three in the morning. He glanced rapidly at the list of names. Not many were persons of rank or birth. Mostly they were shop-assistants, servants, seamen. His search for the malefactor would be so much the easier. Liljensparre was a student of human nature, and knew already which circles he would have to look in to find the culprit. And it wouldn't be among servants or shop-assistants.

Or had the assassin got away before the doors were closed? The loaded pistol had been found near the exit. The Chief of

Police had misgivings. Perhaps, when all was said and done, all this listing of names had been futile? Two witnesses had already been heard: the trumpeter Örnberg, and the servant Fagerberg. Both had described in some detail the assailant's mask; their accounts differed. While Fagerberg described him as rather short of stature, others had been saying he was a tall, well-built man. Which was also the king's impression.

Now the men on the windlass were lowering the great crystal chandelier from the ceiling and the candles were being snuffed. Liljensparre, his procurators and his policemen packed up their belongings. In their sledges they drove the short distance over the bridge, round the Palace, to the police headquarters on Slottsbacken.

It was quite possible, of course, that the assassin was already outside the city. Some little time must necessarily have passed before the Light Dragoons could post themselves at all the barriers. But the Chief of Police did not despair. He had the *corpus delicti* in his possession. He laid the three weapons out in a row on his table. How the black-painted knife came into the hands of a murderer, he supposed, would forever defy elucidation: it was a perfectly ordinary crude kitchen knife, such as could be found in thousands of Stockholm homes. With the demi-pistols it was different.

The Chief of Police took out a list of all the gunsmiths and makers of pistols in Stockholm. Altogether they numbered no more than twenty-six. Of swordsmiths, only five. The clothiers, too, who hired out costumes for masquerades, would also have to be interrogated. No stone must be left unturned.

Liljensparre called in some of his assistants, and told them to go and wake up all the gunsmiths and swordsmiths in the city. Notwithstanding the inconvenience of the hour, they were to ask them if by any chance they had recently sold a pair of Wåhlberg pistols.

At four o'clock, after a few hours' rest, Soldier No.21, Smith, relieved No.85, Lindström, at his post outside Lilliehorn's house on the square, opposite the Opera. While they were standing there chatting in the darkness a window was thrown open in the lieutenant-colonel's house, and the servant, Krantz, looked out.

'When was the king shot?' he asked.

Smith turned.

'Can't say exactly. Must have been between eleven and twelve o'clock, when I was last on duty here.'

Krantz uttered a flat hollow laugh and slammed shut the window.

VII

SWIFT EXPOSURES

About six o'clock that morning Anckarström was awakened by someone knocking at his door. To his relief he found it was only Captain Gyllencreutz's servant; it had been agreed he should borrow a sledge and harness for his master, who had planned a trip into the country. In his cold room Anckarström dressed hastily, put on his grey overcoat and broad-brimmed hat; with Gyllencreutz's servant he went across the narrow yard to the part of the building which overlooked the street and mounted the stairs. There he sat down and wrote out instructions as to where the sledge and its harness were to be found.

'Have you heard the dreadful news, Captain, about what happened at last night's masked ball?' the servant asked. 'They say someone's shot the king.'

If Captain Gyllencreutz's servant expected this news to come as a surprise, he was disappointed. Anckarström, without so much as answering, handed him the scrap of paper. Naturally, thought the servant, he must have heard it from the maid. And with a clumsy bow took his leave.

In the children's room the little girl, the three-year-old, was shouting for Anna. The little boys were already at play; he could hear their bare feet chasing one another round the room. In the kitchen Elsa was banging her pots and pans on the mantelpiece. Soon the gruel would be on the table. Anckarström hung about the house and had breakfast with his children. Anna dandled the youngest on her knee as she fed her.

'Lord!' she exclaimed suddenly. 'And I haven't lit your fire, Captain! You forgot to give me the key to your room last night.'

'I'll light it myself,' said Anckarström curtly. Getting up from the table, he put on his outdoor clothes and went out. The whole city was swathed in fog. As yet few people were about. Reaching the Haymarket, he rounded the Riding School and went on up Spektene Hill over the ridge and down to the alley of Ålandsgränden. A relief patrol came riding by at smart trot northwards, towards the Roslagen Barrier. At a street corner where a notice had just been posted up he saw a couple of old fellows painstakingly spelling out the bulletin and heard them calling down woe and damnation upon all godless malefactors.

Anckarström was on his way to his brother Gustaf, a cavalry major, who lived in Packartorgsgatan*. Feelings between the two men had long been strained. The cause had usually been Jakob's miserliness. His brother had a claim against him of more than four thousand *riksdalers*. By chance he ran into him in Norrlandsgatan.

'Come along home with me, and we'll sort out our business in peace and quiet,' Gustaf said.

'That's of no importance. I've something else to tell you.'

His brother stared at him in surprise.

'I've done something, you see,' Jakob Johan went on, 'which means I'm in danger. If they arrest me you'll have to look after my affairs.'

Gustaf was troubled to see his brother was speaking in deadly earnest. He did not mince matters:

'Why should you be arrested?'

'If I am, you'll know soon enough.'

This was not good enough for his brother. He insisted on knowing the truth.

'Haven't you heard about the king being wounded at the masquerade?'

'Wounded!'

'Yes, that's the way of it,' said Jakob Johan.

(*) Near the present Nybroplan. (Transl.)

The cavalry major had been on his way to the Haymarket to buy hay. Now he had something more serious to think about. As they walked towards Packartorgsgatan together, his brother's brief account made him realize all too well what sort of peril he must be in, and the catastrophe hanging over his family. Immediately the roles were reversed. Instead of demanding payment or being adamant about interest and amortization, Gustaf perceived that Jakob Johan stood in urgent need of someone whom he could trust with whatever could now be saved of his fortune.

The capital awoke. From the roofs of tumbledown old houses around St John's chapel the chimney smoke drifted up towards the grey sky. Fires had been lit in earthenware stoves. Water was being fetched from wells. Arriving two by two at the wells with their water-buckets slung from a pole between them, serving-maids were told the news – and made such haste to get home again that they spilled half the water. Here was something for mistress! Some had already heard it.

The most assiduous of all the town's newspaper editors and busiest of its many busy letter-writers and diarists, Assessor Carl Christoffer Gjörwell, lived at the far end of Regeringsgatan. He was awakened by his maid. As usual, she had brought him a bowl of warm water, to bathe his tired eyes.

'My, but the mistress had a *dreadful* night at the masquerade, sir!' she said, letting her tongue linger on each succulent word.

'Dreadful? How?' asked Gjörwell tetchily.

'Oh, sir – summat awful's happened!'

'Something? What thing?' exploded her master, exasperated.

'They've shot the king!

'My God! What's that you say?' Terrified, the sixty-year-old writer fell back on his bed.

'Yes, sir. He's been shot with a pistol.'

Gjörwell's first thought, too, was that the deed could only

have been done by the Jacobinical actor La Perrière. Hurrying in to his wife, Brita Nora, Gjörwell heard the whole story. When at last she had got home after having had her name written down on Liljensparre's list, she hadn't had the heart to wake her husband. Plunged into painful reflections, Gjörwell dressed, intending to hurry down-town to hear how things were with the king. But seeing the slippery state of the roads after yesterday's thaw and the ensuing night-frost, he sent his maid down to Norrmalmstorg to get him a sledge.

There she found several policemen. They were writing down the names of everyone who wanted to hire a sledge. A corporal was deciding whether permission should be granted or withheld. When the maid said it was for Assessor Gjörwell, he gave a friendly nod.

'Assessor Gjörwell? Yes, of course he can have a sledge.'

Everywhere in the city and out in the suburbs the same scenes were being repeated. Everywhere the news provoked indignation, sometimes affected, sometimes heartfelt. And almost everywhere it was the servant girls who were spreading the news. At Trångsund, in the Old Town, Johan Albrekt Ehrenström, recorder of the Supreme Court, had been enjoying a well-earned night's rest after dealing with the foreign mail the previous evening. In the morning he, too, was awakened by his manservant, who had already been out.

In a terrified voice the latter announced the news:

'What a disaster! The king's been shot!'

'Are you mad?'

'No, worse luck, it's true, what I say.'

'Who told you?'

'The king's own servants and people who're standing about weeping outside the Palace.'

Ehrenström quickly drew on his clothes to hurry up to the Palace; he called to mind a little episode of the previous evening: he and Jakob von Engeström, together with their servants, walking in single file with their lanterns, had been taken for a funeral procession. In retrospect the incident seemed to have been an omen of approaching disaster.

Thoroughly and at great length Anckarström and his brother discussed what should be done. Then the captain went straight home. His servants had heard the rumour from a woman who sold milk. Anxiously they enquired whether it was true. Anckarström could not deny it. Going up to his room overlooking the yard, he lit a fire in his stove and sat down beside it to watch the wood catch. But his restlessness grew and grew. Solitude was too much for him. Going out into the streets again, he followed the same route as before and at the well on Smedjegatan fell in with a cavalry major, by name Mathias Ribben. For a while they stood chatting together.

Now it was eight o'clock. In the great chamber of the Court of Appeal, inside the old palace on Riddarholmen island, the perplexed judges and their assistants, summoned by Lord Chancellor Wachtmeister, who was also their president, were sitting down round their long table. Wachtmeister explained the reasons for the plenum. With a pistol shot an unidentified mask had wounded the king in his left side, just above the thigh. Yet with the Almighty's help there was still hope the king's precious life might be saved. Although wounded, the king was strong enough to walk upstairs from the stage. And when about to be moved to the Palace he had wanted to go down the stairs on foot. Only on the doctor's advice had he allowed himself to be carried.

The miscreant, alas, had escaped, the Lord Chancellor went on. Now the king's orders were that the court should proclaim a reward of 25,000 *riksdalers* to anyone apprehending him, or 10,000 *riksdalers* to anyone helping the investigators with accurate information. The offer was to be announced to beat of drum from a sledge, escorted by a piquet of the Guards all over the city. It would also be printed, and on the morrow, a Sunday, read out in all churches, both in the city and in all neighbouring parishes. These decisions made, the Lord Chancellor hastily left the room to wait upon the king.

In language expressive of its indignation at the hateful deed, the court immediately got down to work:

In view of the terrible events of the past night in the auditorium of the Opera House, whereby a person destitute of all honour, clad in a black domino costume, masked and wearing a round hat on his head, fired a pistol at the king's precious person, thereby wounding the king; and inasmuch as the aforesaid unknown miscreant immediately contrived to escape in the crowd after dropping the discharged pistol as well as another similar weapon loaded with bullet and shot, and a dagger, in shape like unto a coarse kitchen knife, with a sharp point and made jagged on both edges and on one side barbed: let this unknown horrible miscreant be generally sought for, and any person or persons having knowlege of him, his place of abode or of his fellow-criminals forthwith on pain of severe punishment give utterance to the same here in Stockholm at the offices of the City Governor; or, in the provinces, to the king's military commander –

While the quill pens were being sharpened to formulate this royal proclamation, the Vice-President of the Court and one of its justices had gone to the Palace, there to inquire on behalf of the Court after the king's health. Suddenly they returned with orders from the Lord Chancellor. The proclamation was not to be issued for the time being. He had heard that the miscreant had been caught. The Court's meeting was adjourned until a quarter to three that afternoon.

To go from house to house and wake up all the gunsmiths and swordsmiths and clothiers in Stockholm and get them to try to call to mind whether they had had anything to do with the Wåhlberg pistols was a time-consuming business. After all, every single officer of the garrison was armed, either with two service pistols or with two small pocket pistols of the same sort. After the Finnish Campaign, many had recently been buying new pistols, or handing in their old ones for repair.

But by and by, as he went from one gunsmith's shop to another, a policeman by name of Jenner had arrived at Västra Bangränd alley, near the Riding School at the Haymarket. Here a pistol-maker, Anders David Kauffman, had his workshop. Had he had anything to do with Wåhlberg pistols? To the joy of the exhausted policeman, the answer was yes. Kauffman did remember, very clearly, having repaired just such a pair and providing one of the two with a new stock. But on whose account? Here the answer was reluctant and less certain.

'A nobleman.'

More he could not tell. But from Kauffman's anxious reticence the policeman concluded he knew more than he was willing to say. So he had ordered him to accompany him to the offices of the Governor, where Liljensparre had continued the interrogation. Excitement was running high now in the police office.

'It was a nobleman who had just come back from Gävle.'

'What was his name?'

Kauffman's answer took such a long time in coming that only with difficulty could the hot-tempered Liljensparre control himself.

'I daren't say the name,' the pistol-maker replied. 'If I do, I can get into all sorts of trouble.

Just what he meant by those words Kauffman never explained. To 'split' on a dismissed captain, a man virtually without social influence who to the populace's curses would be sent to lose his head on Gallows Hill, could hardly get anyone into trouble. Perhaps Kauffman knew the expensive pistols with their rococo engravings had been in the possession of Horn, a nobleman of high birth; and that if he named the murderer's name, this could lead to other names being mentioned? And that, for someone who was pistol-maker to the Royal Life Guards, could really be a risky matter.

Liljensparre pressed him. Didn't the fellow realize what was in question – the arrest of someone guilty of the worst crime any human being could possibly commit, next to blasphemy? At this Kauffman said the nobleman's name was Jakob Johan Anckarström. Some little while before the Gävle *riksdag* he'd come into the shop and handed the pistols to his apprentice. The firelocks were to be mended: they must not misfire. Kauffman himself had been out at the time; but he recalled the order because Anckarström had come back to fetch them a day or so before leaving for Gävle; but the pistols had not been ready. Not until he returned from Gävle had he got them back.

'Are you acquainted with Captain Anckarström?' Liljensparre's voice was no longer sharp or threatening.

'By sight, very well. I've seen him about ever since I was a boy, when I was foster-child and prentice in Wåhlberg the pistol-smith's house by the Tiltyard. Besides, I sold a couple of pistols to his brother, the cavalry major, just before the Gävle *riksdag*.'

This was all Liljensparre needed to know. The assassin was exposed. That the pistol found by the Queen's Box had been re-stocked was obvious. The work was shoddier than on the other pistol. Liljensparre recalled, too, that a man by the name of Anckarström had been one of the last guests to be listed at the masked ball.

A few minutes later an officer with assistants was on his way to Gamla Kungsholmsbrogatan. They found the man they were looking for at home. They told him they were to take him to the police office for interrogation. He made no objections. Jakob Anckarström, dismissed guards captain, had already given up.

While Liljensparre had been waiting for his emissaries to return, a cake-maker's servant had come, asking to speak with him on urgent business. He was a young fellow of twenty or so. His name, he said, was Petter Bark. Anxiously twisting his leather cap in his hands, he told hesitantly how the previous evening, about one hour before the king's arrival, he had been standing in the vestibule of the Opera when someone had asked him to hand a note to Rémy, a footman of the Royal chamber, and offered him two *riksdalers* for his trouble. But he had never found Rémy; and when he got back to the vestibule the man was no longer there.

This was valuable information. This missive, Liljensparre realized, could have been none other than the warning letter. The baker's boy looked honest enough, but it hardly seemed as if he had contacted the police voluntarily. And indeed, he admitted, he had hesitated a long while; but a magistrate who lodged at the baker's house had ordered him to go straight to the Chief of Police.

'How was he dressed? The man who gave you the note, I mean?'

'In a blue overcoat.'

Liljensparre sighed. If he was to suspect all wearers of blue overcoats it would be like looking for a needle in a haystack.

'Could you recognize the man who gave you the note from his stature, his way of speaking, or anything else?'

'Ye-es' replied Petter Bark, hesitantly. 'He was a solidly-built, good-looking fellow with rather a chubby face. As far as I could judge in the haste and the darkness he looked like Lilliehorn.'

'Lieutenant-Colonel Lilliehorn?'

The baker's boy nodded. It was him, he was almost sure. The guards on duty in the vestibule had thought so too.

'So – you never got your reward?' Liljensparre went on, frowning. 'Listen to me. You are to go to his room and demand your *riksdalers*. Do it in such a way that he won't suspect you've been sent – as if you were doing it of your own accord. And then come straight here and let me hear what has happened.'

This was an order, and no matter how scared the boy might be of having to witness before a court, it must be obeyed. So off he went to Norrmalmstorg. Seeing how unsure he was of himself, the Chief of Police sent one of his men to accompany him as far as the front door – for safety's sake.

Petter Bark was admitted by Krantz, the footman. Lilliehorn came to meet him in the drawing room, but gave not the faintest sign of recognizing him. As the boy began mumbling something about the letter, the lieutenant-colonel, gripping the sleeve of his coat, dragged him out into the vestibule, where Krantz could hear what was being said.

'Are you out of your wits, boy, or are you dreaming?' he hissed.

Bark repeated his demand for payment.

'Do you know me? Do you know who I am?'

'Yes,' stammered the bewildered boy. 'But if I've mistaken you for someone else, sir, I suppose I'll have to go without my *riksdalers*.'

After the door had slammed behind his unwelcome visitor, Lilliehorn was assailed by a most disagreeable feeling. Obviously, all his precautions had been in vain. He'd been recognized. And if that half-wit boy went and gossiped to one of Liljensparre's henchmen, he could find himself in a very tight spot.

Looking at the clock, Lilliehorn saw it was nearly ten o'clock. Time for him to go on parade. He ordered Krantz to fetch him his uniform and boots. Confronted with the courtiers, he wished above all to give an appearance of frankness and honesty. What had he to fear, anyway? Was it not he who had tried to prevent the dreadful deed?

As the morning wore on, visitors came crowding into the upper dining room of the Palace. This corner room was only separated from the royal bedchamber by the audience chamber. In the bedchamber were the king's brothers, the Dukes Charles and Fredrik Adolf, all persons on duty at court and in the armed forces, the Adjutant-General Klingspor, and the doctors. At four a.m. the king had been bled. Three hours later a first attempt had been made to operate. All they had been able to extract from the wound had been the heads of two nails. So the bullet must have penetrated more deeply than at first had been thought. Although they concealed their anxiety from the public, this worried the doctors.

From von Essen Ehrenström heard a vivid account of all that had occurred at the Opera.

'But why didn't you try to prevent the king from going to the masquerade, then?' Ehrenström exclaimed.

'What good could it have done? You know very well he has always despised anonymous letters. In his desk he has a whole drawer full of them. It would have been quite useless. He has always thought people were only trying to test his courage. Most of all he has feared appearing to be afraid.'

'But when you saw the masks below the grille, from the box? Why wasn't anything done? He needn't have known about it.'

'How could I have imagined anyone doing such a thing? And what security measures could have been effective among all those masks, crowding round him? And him so easy to recognize?'

Disapprovingly, some bystanders listened to Essen making his excuses.

The Secretary of State, Elis Schröderheim, entered the dining room. Conscious of his status of favourite with the king, he held his head high. He had not been at the masquerade; had only heard what had happened the morning after. Not many minutes passed before he was commanded to enter the bedchamber.

The king, turned on his right side and resting on his right arm, was lying on the left side of the great bed. He seemed to have a healthy colour. Schröderheim tried to conceal his own anxiety; but the king noticed it and held out his hand. His voice was unchanged.

'Good morning, my dear Schröderheim! Have courage! They don't think the wound is all that serious, seeing I've been able to walk. The outcome is uncertain; but if I come back, remember what I'm telling you now: the opposition's days are numbered. Mostly it depends on myself whether the rest of my days are to be tranquil.'

The king asked Schröderheim whether the attempt on his life was generally known; and what people were saying. But at that moment Acrel and the other doctors were announced. They were waiting to probe the wound. Schröderheim had to leave the bedchamber.

Meanwhile the parade had come to an end, and some senior officers came up to the dining room to wait upon the king. At their head was Lieutenant-Colonel Pontus Lilliehorn. A close friend of Ehrenström, who had commended him to the king for his bravery during the Finnish campaign, he felt himself to be somewhat in his debt. Seeing Ehrenström standing by the window deep in gloomy thoughts, Lilliehorn went up to him and said how indignant he was at the monstrous deed.

'If any Swede has had any part in it,' Lilliehorn said, 'it will dishonour the entire Swedish nation.' Ehrenström agreed. Like many others, he had the very highest respect for Lilliehorn.

In the great ceremonial bed of state the doctors probed the wound. At the king's orders, General Taube, Fredrik Sparre and Johan Gabriel Oxenstierna were also present. But the doctors had no success in extracting the bullet. They tried to console Duke Charles by telling him that, in passing into His Majesty's body, it might have taken such a direction that it could be left there without endangering his life. They cited many cases of people sustaining gunshot wounds and living to a ripe old age.

The king bore the torment of their examination without complaint. After it was over, hearing that the officer corps had come up to the Palace, he summoned Lieutenant-Colonel

Lilliehorn.

'My dear Pontus, whoever would have thought a murderer's bullet would put me on my sick-bed, after escaping so many dangers in the war?'

Twice Lilliehorn kissed the king's outstretched hand and expressed his repugnance at the deed. Then, returning to the dining room, he went on talking to Ehrenström.

There a great many people had assembled. The Lord Chancellor, too, had come up from the court. All spoke together in whispers. All of a sudden, through the open door from the hall of the bodyguard, the Chief of Police came in. In his resonant voice he announced:

'The assailant has been discovered and arrested!'

Everyone crowded round, asked who it was.

'He's a Swedish nobleman, a former captain in the Yellow Guard. His name – Anckarström.'

To most people the name meant nothing. Anckarström did not move in court circles. And having left the service so long ago, he was not an associate of the officers either. But one of those present said:

'He has a savage nature.'

By now the night's dreadful event was known all over the city. On streets, in market-places, indignant people were gathering, eager to hear more. And everywhere the blue and yellow uniforms of the cavalry of the National Guard wearing white royalist armbands were appearing, to keep the peace.

At long last Gjörwell had got his sledge and driven down into the town. There he was consoled with the news that the king's wound was not mortal, and that there were hopes of his recovery. Paying the hastiest of visits to his Historical Bookshop, he was too agitated to stay long, and ordered the cabby to drive him back to Regeringsgatan. On the wall of a house in Storkyrkobrinken, in the Old Town, he noticed someone putting up a bulletin about the king's condition. Already it was attracting a small crowd. Getting quickly out of his sledge, Gjörwell went over to see what it said. Suddenly he heard a voice behind him say:

'They've caught the assassin!'

'Who?' asked Gjörwell, turning round. A lieutenant was standing behind him.

'I'll tell you who it is. It's Captain Anckarström.'

'Jesus!'

Throwing himself into his sledge, Gjörwell rode home. It was as if a dagger had been thrust into his heart. The rumour had already reached his wife. Both burst into tears. If anyone had reason to feel deeply shaken, it was Gjörwell. In his youth he had been a close friend of the assassin's father, a wealthy lieutenant-colonel who had owned an estate on Lindö. Together they had started publishing a French-Swedish dictionary. And when at the age of five Anckarström had lost his tyrannical father – tyrannical, that is, towards his children – Gjörwell had become the boy's guardian. Afterwards Gjörwell had been repelled by Jakob Johan's uninhibited greed for money, and their ways had parted. But his marriage had made them relatives. Anckarström's mother-in-law, Margareta Löwen, was Gjörwell's cousin.

The slaying of the king was to have been the condition for a revolution. But the king was still alive, and no signal for revolt had been given. The conspirators fell prey to the most dreadful anxiety. Hour after hour through the long night many of them had walked the streets, ready when the hour struck to incite the people against the royal tyranny. But now the tyrant was lying on his sick-bed in the Palace. And everywhere on streets and market places people were gathering with oaths and curses on their lips. But it was not the tyrant whom they hated – it was those who had sought his life.

Supposing Gustaf was not as hated as they had blindly believed? Could they have been so deeply mistaken about the popular mood? When all was said and done, the king was perhaps not such a monster as they had thought? All of a sudden the populace seemed to have forgiven him his frivolity, his wastefulness, and were remembering only his great human qualities, his gentle disposition, and his attempts to crush the arrogance of the aristocracy.

The conspirators felt the ground quaking under their feet. How could they escape entanglement in the nets of Liljensparre – that much-feared man? Some of the boldest went up to the Palace and wrote their names in the visitors' lists. Claes Horn did so. Ribbing and his cousin Knut Kurck likewise. But others took the road to Blasieholmen. No longer was General Pechlin's door locked. At his dinner table Bielke, Plomgren, Strussenfelt and Hierta gathered. Hardly had they sat down to talk than a relative of the general arrived. Anckarström, he announced, had already been caught and was in prison.

The younger officers hardly knew how to conceal their dismay. Thure Bielke, suddenly remembering the letter he had written and already posted off to his son-in-law, Captain von Baumgarten at Ryningsnäs, in faraway Småland, fell into a panic. He had been obliged to put off his promised journey home, he had written, 'having been invited to share a Spanish cake'. In his certainty that the tyrant would be cleared out of the way and the revolution succeed, he had added that, if his son-in-law wanted to have a sniff at this banquet, he could by and by come up to the capital. These were dangerous, audacious words. All mail posted on Friday, he knew, had been impounded and brought back to the police office in Stockholm. Supposing von Baumgarten was interrogated? What would he say of this allusion to a 'feast'? The accursed letter gave Bielke no peace. The only person to keep his head was the host himself. He began speaking of Sweden's misfortune and the dreadful results which must ensue from the unheard of thing that had taken place. His words were ambiguous. For they could also mean, of course, the exact opposite: that the country's misfortune would have been less had the king been killed and the revolution succeeded.

In the afternoon, at a quarter to three, the court again assembled. This time the Chancellor of Justice, Herman af Låstbom, was also present. The president of the court confirmed what everyone already knew: that Anckarström had confessed and was to be subjected to a preliminary interrogation. The door opened and Liljensparre and Adjutant-General Klingspor entered. The latter reported that the prisoner had just been brought from the police office to the court, under such safe escort that he could neither do himself any harm nor escape.

Liljensparre showed the astonished gentlemen the murder weapons, laying out before them on the table the sharply-whetted black-handled kitchen knife, with its barbed upper edge. Proudly he exposed to their view the two walnut demi-pistols, with their gleaming fittings, the *corpora delicti* that had given him the brilliant idea of contacting every pistol-maker in Stockholm, with such swift results. Only eight hours had passed since the murder. Yet already the murderer was under lock and key and he had his confession in his hands.

'I've had the charge of the unfired pistol removed,' said Liljensparre, 'and taken out its contents.'

He held up an envelope, broke its seal; and on to the table top poured out a mass of little pieces of metal.

'As you see, the charge consists of gunpowder, a round unpolished lead ball, another ball flattened on two sides and roughened at one end; further, ten coarse pellets of small-shot, four rough and sharp-edged rings and a so-called plug of leather. Also another plug of grey paper. This carpet-tack, however, was found in the king's clothes. It belongs to the other shot.'

The judges and assessors had risen from their chairs and were craning out over the table to get a better view. Horrified, they imagined what would have happened if this shot, too, had been fired into the king's back. At least there was hope – God willing – that he would survive.

'The barb on the knife,' Liljensparre went on, holding up the dagger; 'Anckarström says he cut it out in order to make the blow more dangerous and incurable. He has been alone in committing the crime, so he alleges. Quite alone.'

The justices of the court whispered together, and some shook their wigs; but fell silent when the president ordered the arrested man to be brought in. But Liljensparre had one more trump to play. He told of the baker's boy's visit to Lilliehorn.

'What's the boy's name?' asked the President.

'He requests that what he has to say may remain confidential,' declared Liljensparre. Privately he was reflecting that this was the second witness anxious to preserve his anonymity.

'He will have to be examined before the court!'

The Chief of Police was of the same opinion; he gave the name of the baker's boy. At a sign from the president the doors were thrown open and Anckarström, closely guarded, was led in. The notary, who was dutifully keeping the minutes, scratched down his observations. The accused, he found, was of medium height, short rather than tall, and appeared to be physically strong.

In a serious voice the president exhorted him to give a veracious and honest confession, withholding nothing. First he wished to know Anckarström's personal details. And Anckarström, partly of his own accord, and partly in answer to repeated questions, said he was born in 1762 at Lindö Manor, in Vallentuna hundred, son of Lieutenant-Colonel Jakob Johan Anckarström and his wife, Hedvig Drufva, daughter of the provincial governor. He had lost his mother at an early age. At the age of eight he had been sent to the University at Uppsala and seven years later, on the death of his father, had been accepted at court as a page.

Two of the judges whispered together. A page? He could

never have been that. It simply wasn't true.

His military career had begun as a volunteer in the Royal Lifeguards: Trooper No. 38, Nälen depot, attached to his father's estate. In 1775, at the age of thirteen, he had been promoted corporal, but three years later had resigned from the cavalry and become an ensign in the lifeguards. In 1783 he had finished his military career and been granted his release with honorary rank of captain, when he had married Gustaviana Elisabeth Löwen. He had moved to an official dwelling at Mellösa, in his own part of the country, and thence to Thorsåker Manor, which he had rented from Major Olof Rudbeck. But after quarrelling with the latter about the lease, he had moved back to Stockholm. Anckarström then told the court about his ill-fated journey to the island of Gotland and the brow-beating to which he had been subjected during his interrogation at that time.

Apparently unmoved, neither sombre nor depressed, Anckarström said the charge of high treason had thrown him into despair. If he had wished to end the king's days, it had been to help his country.

'But it's impossible that what happened to you in Gotland should have given you such hatred for the king,' objected the president. 'Your case has still not come up before him.'

'Yes, it did,' Anckarström insisted. 'One reason for my action has been the rough way I was treated by the crown's servants and the peasants on Gotland.'

He cast a glance at Låstbom. It had been at the latter's instigation he and Runeberg had been sent under guard to Visby. Then he resumed his narrative.

He had planned the murder two days before the masked ball that was to have taken place on 9 March. He had spoken to no one. Hadn't wished to confide in folk who talked but did nothing. Eight or ten days ago he had bought a knife at the ironmonger's on Riddarhustorget. Powder and shot he had at home. On Friday evening he had cast lead bullets and loaded his pistols and at about half-past nine, clad in his fancy dress, had gone, all by himself, to the Opera House. He had felt no remorse, rather relief at being able to serve his country. Had he succeeded in killing the king, he would have shot himself with the second pistol he had in his right-hand trouser pocket.

'Why didn't you shoot yourself, then, as you'd intended?'

'In my confusion at the shot not proving mortal, I thought I could hide. But I failed to get out, and had to unmask like all the others, and stay in the theatre until morning.'

'What did you do next?'

'I went home and slept for a couple of hours.'

He told of his meeting with his brother in Norrlandsgatan and how he had asked him to take charge of his affairs, should he be taken. He also mentioned his meeting with Major Ribben.

'With him,' interposed Liljensparre, suspiciously, 'you had, so I have heard, a very intimate conversation.'

'It concerned private matters, only. Then I went home again and stayed there until I was called to the Governor's offices.'

Liljensparre showed him the knife and pistols.

'How strongly charged was the pistol you fired?'

'An inch of powder and two balls. About six lead shot and six broken carpet tacks.'

'Why did you put more powder in the shot you intended for the king?'

'To make sure it would kill him.'

All this time Anckarström had been speaking with a frankness intended to leave no doubt about the truth of his narrative. But Liljensparre was not so easily convinced.

'From your examination this morning it transpired that, some eight days or a fortnight before the *riksdag* in Gävle, you had Kauffman repair and re-stock the pistols. Were you already thinking of committing this awful crime?'

'No, like so many other noblemen, I wanted to have pistols with me on the journey. When I didn't get them back from

Kauffman I got hold of another pair.'

'During your interrogation you admitted having spoken to someone at the masquerade.'

'I said so, but my memory failed me. It wasn't until afterwards.'

'Fagerberg, the footman, anyway, had stated he saw you in company with a number of other masks. Can't you see how absurd it is to pretend you had no accomplices? The note warning the king, too, shows that others knew of the plan to kill him.'

'I have no accomplices,' Anckarström insisted obstinately.

'What do you mean by "the opposition", then? In the interrogation it says you thought you would be honoured for your deed by the *opposition*.'

'I never said that! Or at least I didn't mean it. I thought I would be honoured by the *nation*. With the king out of the way I thought the nation would become more united. And I would also profit from bank coin again coming into circulation, instead of the national debt notes. These thoughts first lodged in my heart during the *riksdag* after it had been decided that bank loans were to be repayable in national debt notes. If the king died, the country's economy would be administered better.'

Angrily the president intervened:

'By your mistaken idea that the *nation* would honour so hateful a deed you've cast a monstous shadow over all the inhabitants of the realm! No, Captain Anckarström, it seems more credible you said 'opposition', and were referring to some accomplices. It is your duty to tell us who they are.'

All eyes turned to Anckarström. Defiantly he shook his head.

'If I said "opposition", it was by mistake.'

Further than that it seemed impossible to get. So the accused was taken out. At the request of Vice-Governor Ahlman – whose iron hand had led the peasants at the *riksdag* – it was decided that to avoid risky journeys from the police office down to Riddarholmen where the court sat, Anckarström should be kept in one of the rooms of the courthouse, on the other side of the vestibule. To humiliate him further he was to be kept in handcuffs and with fettered legs.

So the culprit was under lock and key. Soldiers with fixed bayonets surrounded the house where the court was sitting. And the whole of Riddarholmen Island was under military surveillance. But wasn't Anckarström a mere tool in the hands of greater forces? His early-morning meeting with his brother seemed suspect, as did his intimate conversation with Major Ribben in Norra Smedjegatan. And whose errand had the baker's boy been running? All these people were summoned for interrogation. First in turn was Petter Bark.

He told of his encounter with the gentleman in the blue overcoat. And of his visit to his home during the morning. Having nothing more to say, the lad was allowed to go. Of course, he might have got hold of the wrong person. So, at least, thought some of the judges, for whom Lilliehorn was a man above reproach. Liljensparre, however, kept his thoughts to himself. Now it was Major Gustaf Anckarström's turn to be called in.

'Between seven and eight o'clock this morning,' he began, 'I was walking from where I live at tanner Setterström's in Packartorgsgatan, to buy hay. In the alley between Packartorget and Regeringsgatan I met my wretched brother. I asked him to come home with me, to have a chat about money matters, but he asked me whether I knew of the king being shot or wounded at the masquerade – I was so upset I don't remember his exact words. Then we parted.'

'Your brother has told a different story. He is said to have asked you, Major, to look after his household if anything should happen to him.'

'He never asked me any such thing,' declared the major.

'When did you meet?'

'Some time between seven and eight, I've said.'

Gustaf Anckarström was permitted to retire. And since there was no one else to interrogate they broke up.

Horn was at his sister-in-law's. Anckarström's swift capture and confession had given him a nasty shock, but he relied on him not to betray anyone. Worst of all was that the previous evening he had left his purple overcoat in Anckarström's room, where Liljensparre and his henchmen were just now busy poking about. At that moment, as a friend in need, Major Gustaf Anckarström turned up. The real purpose of his visit was to hide away part of Jakob's fortune, placed early that morning in the hands of a sympathetic woman. Horn prevailed on him to say the overcoat was his. For a brother to say he had forgotten it would be less likely to arouse suspicion.

So Ulla Linnerhjelm, never at a loss, sent Jakob Johan's maid to fetch it. The maid had no success, and so Ulla had to go herself. But however much she flirted with the policemen, or however humbly she appealed to them, she, too, had to leave empty-handed. Everything had been impounded. All this sudden interest in the overcoat, however, aroused Liljensparre's suspicions. Obviously, someone had changed his clothes at the same time as the assassin, and in his room. In a cold Swedish winter no one goes about without an overcoat. Next time he interrogated Anckarström he would ask him about it.

The rumour that a warning note had come into the king's hands had spread quickly, and when Ehrenström went to see his friend Abraham Niklas Edelkrantz – who as director of the Royal Theatre lived in the Opera House – he inquired curiously who could have written it.

'That's already known,' said Edelkrantz.

'Who, then?'

'Pontus Lilliehorn. Baron Armfelt told me so. I met him

before leaving the Palace, about three o'clock.'

'How can they suspect Lilliehorn of such a thing!'

It was more than Ehrenström could grasp. Getting up from the sofa, he went over to a window from which he had a view of the square. Lilliehorn, he saw, had opened one of his windows and was leaning out.

'Come over here,' he remarked to his friend. 'Do you think Lilliehorn looks like a regicide?'

Not long afterwards Ehrenström left. Emerging into the square and walking across it towards Fredsgatan, he could see Lilliehorn. He was still in the same attitude. Ehrenström greeted him and Lilliehorn replied: but then he left the window and began striding up and down in his room.

The Chief of Police went up to the Palace. In the dining room and the outer rooms many people were still gathered waiting to hear about the king's condition. Nothing untoward had occurred. If only the wound continued to suppurate, the pieces of metal in his body would perhaps be expelled; that was the opinion of the doctors in the audience chamber, where they were holding their consultations behind a screen.

On his way out, Liljensparre chanced to see Lilliehorn in the hall of the bodyguard. He requested a word with him, alone, and they went to one side. His sharp penetrating eyes obstinately fixed on the lieutenant-colonel, Liljensparre came straight to the point. He told him he was suspected of being the author of the warning letter. Was the suspicion justified?

'Yes.' Lilliehorn did not hesitate. 'But I did it with the best of intentions. To avert a catastrophe.'

The Chief of Police did not move a muscle or show how gratified he was to get this answer. Under the stiffly curled and powdered wig no flush of colour came to those sallow features, exhausted from the long night's work.

'I assume,' he said cautiously, 'all you had to do with this letter was to expedite it?'

'I both wrote it and with my own hand signed it.'

They were standing close to a window. On a slip of paper Lilliehorn scribbled a few words with a lead pencil. The handwriting matched.

'What seal did you use?'

'My own. One I once had made in my youth, as a member of a secret freemasonry.'

Lilliehorn took the seal out of his pocket and handed it to the Chief of Police. 'Others' good, my happiness' was its mirrored inscription. The very same words. There was no longer room for doubt.

'And will you also frankly repeat what you've just told me in that place to which I cannot do other than report this matter?'

'Yes. On my word of honour as a gentleman.'

To Lilliehorn it was perfectly clear that the expression 'that place' could only mean a court of law. The Chief of Police, he knew, was a man who acted swiftly. Instead of going home, therefore, he went to the house where Ehrensvärd was living.

'They're on my tracks,' he said hoarsely. 'But I'll never betray you, even if they torture me.'*

This was a consolation. Lilliehorn's strict ideas of honour had always commanded Ehrensvärd's admiration. He had been the one they had all relied on. But that he, while in league with the conspirators, should have sent a warning letter – this shook his faith in him. It was the action of a weak man. Would he prove stauncher when Liljensparre began to snare him with his questions?

Not until about nine o'clock could Liljensparre leave his office and go home to his house in Östra Humlegårdsgatan, in the suburbs. It troubled him that his procurators had not found the lieutenant-colonel at home. If the aristocratic

(*) One of Gustaf III's enlightened acts had been to abolish the use of torture. (Transl.)

league – a term he was fond of using – was keeping, as he much feared it was, a military organization of its own, then Lilliehorn was the most dangerous man of all. His men would follow him to the death.

Liljensparre drove on alone in his hired sledge. The coachman took his route past the darkened Opera House, abandoned now by all the muses of pleasure, and went on down Arsenalsgatan. Some way out on the Ladugårdslandet Bridge a tall officer stepped aside to let them pass. He, too, was on his way out to Ladugårdslandet* and the Chief of Police got no more than a hasty glimpse of his back. But it sufficed.

'Stop!' he shouted to the coachman, and turned in his sledge. 'Lieutenant-Colonel! I have something important to say to you.'

Recognizing Liljensparre's loud voice, Lilliehorn started, but approached the rear of the sledge. Stopping, he put his hand to his sword-hilt. For just a moment Liljensparre – as he long afterwards admitted – was seized with terror. He was entirely unarmed, had no policeman or guard with him. The ragged coachman was not worth much. Never before had he felt so powerless. Suddenly, he got an idea.

'Come with me in the sledge. We'll have a little chat.'

Already he had unbuttoned the foot-sack. To his amazement Lilliehorn, without more ado, got in and sat down beside him. And the horse trotted on again across the long bridge, in the direction of the Artillery Barracks.

'I have the Duke's orders to arrest you.'

'Arrest me!'

That he was acting thus, the Chief of Police went on hastily, was purely out of consideration for Lilliehorn. Had he arrested him in his house and taken him under escort to the guard house, no one, in the present touchy mood of the populace, could say what might have happened. He said

(*) The present Östermalm. (Transl.)

nothing about his reflections as to what disturbances were to be feared from the opposite quarter.

When they reached his house, the Chief of Police immediately ordered out his great covered coach. And the arrested nobleman, hidden from prying eyes, was driven to the guardhouse in the outer palace courtyard.

He was in safe custody. Now it was someone else's turn. The Chief of Police's secret spies had had a great deal to report about the mysterious activities of certain counts, and these would have to be looked into. Again Liljensparre drove home to his suburban house. There he had a tête-à-tête with Claes Horn, with whom he had requested an interview.

Well, what about it? Hadn't the Count been in the habit of associating with Anckarström? Yes, Horn had to admit it.

'I cannot deny I've formed a close friendship with him. Our association became very intimate after he helped me in financial matters. But I never heard him utter a word about his intentions.'

'That overcoat which was left lying in Anckarström's room, was it yours?'

Horn laughed. He had witnessed all the commotion over the overcoat.

'No. It was Major Anckarström's. His brother's.'

'And the domino costume you wore at the masquerade? Where did you hire it?'

'It was my own. It's out at Huvudsta.'

There were other questions, too, to which Liljensparre wished to know the answers. It had come to his ears, for instance, that during the fateful night Horn had been wearing a large sabre. What had he been intending to use that for?

'To protect myself against the peasants.' Horn trotted out the tale he had learned by heart: how he had several times been attacked, and had thereafter always gone armed when on the road. For a while Liljensparre let him go on painting in lurid colours all the dangers attending his journeys to his place in the country. But now came another question:

'The coachman you hired to drive you home last night thought it odd that you were wearing neither an overcoat nor a fur. How was that?'

'My fur was with my servant in my father's tack room. I didn't want to have the bother of it.' Horn gave a little smile. 'Between ourselves, I had other pleasures in mind. Afterwards, in the morning, I could fetch my fur when the servants had begun to curry-comb the horses and the stable stood open.'

Liljensparre did not at all dislike Horn. There was something disarming about his intelligent, aristocratic manner. For a while they went on chatting together, quietly and easily. Then the young count was allowed to go. Whether he went home to his countess, or had other pleasures in mind tonight, too, was no concern of Liljensparre's.

VIII

LILJENSPARRE IS GIVEN A FREE HAND

On Sunday an account of the crime which had been committed against the king's precious person was read out in all the city's churches. The Court of Appeal had no qualms about working on the sabbath. It met after morning service. No one really believed Anckarström's assurances that he alone had been responsible for the deed. All that was now needed was to get him to make a full confession.

Liljensparre presented some startling news. On the Duke's orders he had arrested Lieutenant-Colonel Lilliehorn. The president, too, was able to show them something: the warning letter. He had been given it by the king.

The text contained statements about a widespread conspiracy; and now, as Anckarström was brought in, he was commanded to name his accomplices. But he proved as intractable as he had the day before.

'Truly, it passes my comprehension how the note came into being, or who can have written it. After all, I told no one of my plans. No one can have known anything!'

'Whom have you associated with since the Gävle *riksdag*?'

'I left Gävle the day of the sermon, and arrived in Stockholm on 25 February at six in the morning. That day I was at the house of Colonel Swartzer and the Misses Linnerhjelm and a seamstress called Leus. They live in the same house as myself – Captain Fernström's house in Gamla Kungsholmsbrogatan. At the Linnerhjelm sisters' I met their brother-in-law, Major Claes Horn. Last Wednesday I was out at Horn's place at Huvudsta, to see my eldest daughter, who is living with the count and countess. Apart from these I have few acquaintances. Mostly I come and go in the house of

The scene at the Opera shortly after the wounding of Gustaf (contemporary German engraving).

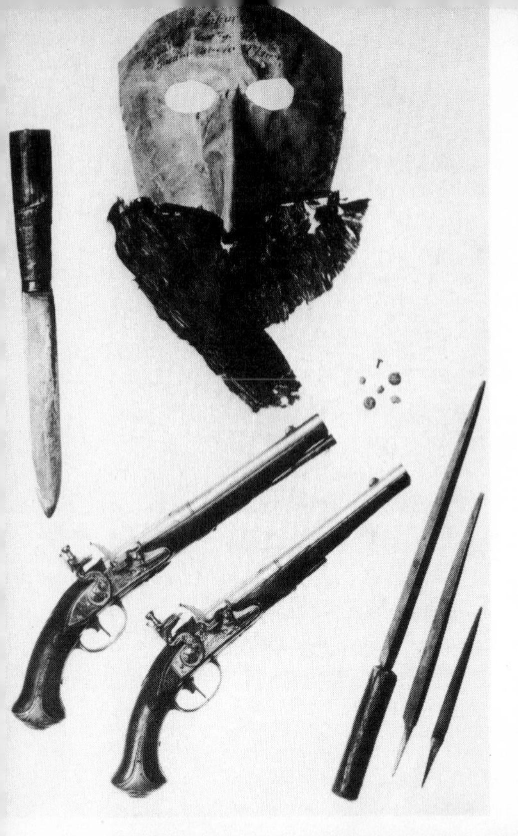

(*Left*) Anckarström's mask and weapons. (*Below*) Gustaf on his death bed attended by the Crown Prince (contemporary German engraving).

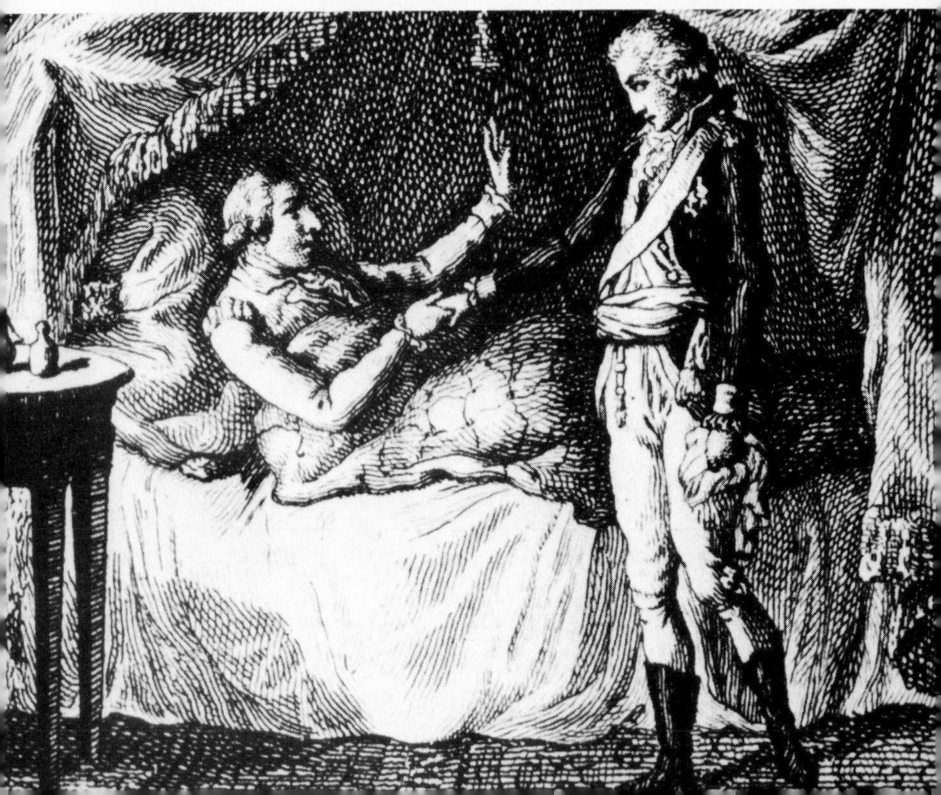

Lieutenant-Colonel Gyllencreutz and his cousin the captain. And of Mr Nordell, the district judge. He had helped me in money matters.'

Liljensparre listened attentively as these names were brought out. About the Gyllencreutzes there was nothing particularly disturbing. But Horn – had he not already interrogated him? His father, the general, was a troublesome old fellow, whom the king had been obliged to arrest in 1789 at the time of the second *coup d'état*. Apples, thought Liljensparre, don't usually fall very far from an apple tree. Nor was he too sure of Nordell.

The Chief of Police's reflections were interrupted by the president's next question. He wanted a fresh account of all the accused's doings on the disastrous Friday. Anckarström replied by telling how, after breakfasting with his children, he had paid a visit to his friends the Gyllencreutzes. How he had sharpened the knife, and loaded his two pistols. His statements about times were so precise, thought Liljensparre, there should be no difficulty in checking them.

'Where did you buy your domino costume?'

'I hired it the same day at Hartin's, the hatters.'

After reflecting a few moments, to Liljensparre's surprise Anckarström added:

'Now I recall that at half-past eight on Friday evening Count Horn came to me to fetch a domino I had also hired for him in Hartin's shop. He had asked me to do it last Wednesday, when I was out at Huvudsta. The count was only in my room a short while, and he can't have seen anything suspicious. Then he went to his sisters-in-law, the Misses Linnerhjelm, and accompanied them to the masquerade.'

'Yesterday you told us about your motives,' the president went on. 'Did you really have no others?'

'My motives were those I have mentioned. Also the Gävle *riksdag*'s decision that bank coin should be repayable in depreciated national debt notes. That depressed and upset me.'

'But the bill came from the secret commission, didn't it? So why should your hatred be directed at the king's person?'

'I got it all wrong,' replied Anckarström in a low voice.

Now the public prosecutor put a question:

'If your dissatisfaction was so great during the *riksdag*, didn't you even at that time begin thinking of carrying out your nefarious designs?'

'No,' said Anckarström. 'Decisions aren't always so quickly arrived at. One idea can grow out of another.'

The prisoner was removed. While the Chief of Police was reflecting that Horn's statements had been quite different, Major Mathias Ribben was brought in. His examination did not yield much:

'In the general consternation yesterday morning, I was walking northwards when I met Captain Anckarström in Malmskillnadsgatan, or perhaps it was Norra Smedjegatan. I asked him whether the rumour was true. Then each of us went his own way.'

'How long have you known Captain Anckarström, Major?'

'I only know him very slightly. In fact, I only know who he is from the days when I was in the Royal Bodyguard and he in the Life Guards. That's nearly ten years ago now.'

His answers were perfectly candid, and he was allowed to go. But there were two more witnesses to be heard before the dinner break: two girls, who in all their simplicity might be able to add something to the picture.

With blushing cheeks the twenty-eight-year-old Elsa Katarina Tyberg was led into the room and curtseyed deeply to the court. On St Michael's Day last, she said, she had come into Anckarström's employment as kitchenmaid. Yes, she knew about the dreadful crime, and could only feel awfully sorry for the misfortune which was to befall her master's four innocent little children, of whom the eldest had just come back from Count Horn's country house. Captain Anckarström's wife was staying with a relative in the country.

'What do you know about your master's crime?'

'Nothing, your lordship,' said Elsa, and shook her head.

'Tell us about his habits.'

'The captain never used to come into the room where his wife lives except to have meals with his children. Mostly he ate out.'

'Have you seen any lead or gunpowder in the home?'

'No, your lordship, never. He lives in the part of the house overlooking the street, and I only went there when I needed money for the housekeeping.'

'Has he had many visitors?'

'I've never seen anyone go there. His room is so uncomfortable.'

'When did he go to the masquerade?'

'I couldn't say exactly. He came home about eight in the evening and had dinner with the children. Then he went back to his room and lay down to sleep. But when he came over to have breakfast, early yesterday morning, I heard he'd been out all night, until six o'clock. Then he went out again and I didn't see him again until the policeman came to fetch him.'

The kitchenmaid was succeeded by the housemaid, Anna Norberg. In the evenings she had been in the habit of following her master up to his room and pulling his boots off for him. Afterwards she had always taken away the key to his room so as to be able to go up early in the morning and make up his fire. But on Friday evening the Captain, most unusually, had kept the key.

'Have you seen any weapons in his possession?'

Anna had to reflect.

'Yes, a fortnight ago I saw a pistol fall out of his pocket when he was putting on his overcoat.'

'Was it one of these?'

Liljensparre held up the pistols found in the Opera House.

'No. I don't recognize them,' said Anna. 'And I didn't see any pocket-pistols in his room last Friday, either, when I was tidying up.'

'Hadn't he packed his things for a journey?'

'No.'

'How did he treat you and the kitchenmaid?'

'He never said much to either of us.'

And that was all they could get out of the housemaid.

In the Old Town crowds of people were drifting about streets and squares, enjoying their Sunday leisure. The blockade of Riddarholmen Island attracted a crowd on Munkbro Quay. They stared up at the heavy façade of the King's House where, thank God, the wretched criminal was under lock and key. A rumour spread. Lilliehorn was to be brought before the court. Everyone rushed over to Storkyrkobrinken. There he came riding down the steep slope in a covered coach.

'Assassin! Regicide!' howled the craftsmen's apprentices, shaking their fists. The market women spat into the melting snow, joining their shrill voices in the cry. But the enraged soldiers of the lieutenant-colonel's own battalion, the Blue-and-Yellows, bawled at them to shut up. Some even ran forward to rescue their beloved chief, but were as quickly thrust aside by the royalist military escort. As the coach reached the Riddarholm Bridge, soldiers with fixed bayonets blocked the paths both of those who wished to liberate the unfortunate man and those who wished only to insult him.

It was three o'clock, and again the court met. Now someone was to be interrogated who should be able to give them more information about all that had happened than any kitchen-maid or housemaid. The door was thrown open, and Lilliehorn was ushered in. His courtly bow and military bearing did nothing to allay their anxiety. His glance, flitting past the gentlemen seated round the table, alighted momentarily on the notary's bent back and returned to the president. Enthroned in his armchair, the latter addressed the witness:

'Yesterday evening, Lieutenant-Colonel, you confessed to

Chief of Police Liljensparre that it was you who wrote the warning note.'

'Yes, Mr President.'

'In that case I must warn you, Lieutenant-Colonel, and in the most serious terms, that it is your duty to tell us with complete frankness about everything leading up to that action. Without concealing anything.'

Lilliehorn cleared his throat.

'With the honesty native to me I will tell you everything. But before I do so I feel I must ask the Royal Court of Appeal to overlook any shortcomings in my manner of expressing myself, inasmuch as I have never stood before a court of law.'

There was a faint stir among the judges' powdered wigs. Everyone knew, of course, that hitherto no crime or breach of duty had ever smirched this guards officer's reputation.

'Early last Friday morning,' Lilliehorn began, 'I heard someone knocking at the door of my drawing room. Since my servant had gone out, I myself went and opened it and saw a lad, about ten or eleven years old, I suppose. He handed me a note. Thinking it must be some begging letter, I took it, and, locking the door, left the boy standing outside. But I was surprised to find that the note was of another sort. As far as I can now remember, its contents ran like this: "It was a shame last Friday's masked ball had been cancelled, for then a good *coup* could have been made at Haga against that restless Personage; but today there's also to be a masquerade and something of consequence is to be done there. Could you be prevailed upon to contribute to this end?" That's how it ran, something of that sort.'

Lilliehorn had hesitated repeatedly, as if having difficulty in recalling the exact content of the letter. Now his words came more evenly:

'When I'd read the note, I immediately opened the door again, but found the boy had gone. I hurried downstairs and called out after him, but got no answer. So I went over to the window of my room and looked out, to see if I could see him; but without result. The thought of the dreadful trap being laid for the king so terrified me that in my utter confusion I didn't know what to do. I thought the *billet* stupid, both in style and manner, but the content was too serious to be ignored. My first impulse was to hurry out to Haga or seek out the king at the Opera and tell him about it verbally. But then I thought that in a letter I could be more circumstantial and that an anonymous letter might have greater effect. So at once I sat down to write one . . . '

'It would have been better if you had not written anonymously,' interposed Liljensparre.

Lilliehorn turned to him.

'As I say, it was originally my intention to hand it to him personally. But I was afraid the king would think I was currying favour, or trying to obtain a reward. So I decided to deliver the letter by an unknown hand.'

Lilliehorn went on to say how, at about ten o'clock in the evening, he had gone out into the square and met a young man of honest appearance, who he thought would not be likely to recognize him. It had been his intention to give him the two *riksdalers* at the same time as the letter, but he had been afraid of being deceived as to his honesty.

'Afterwards, when I heard of the inhuman act which had nevertheless been committed, it was as if a dagger had been plunged into my heart. Only then did I realize that the way I had chosen had not been the best one.'

And that was the end of Pontus Lilliehorn's narrative. On the orders of the Lord Chancellor, the sentence in the anonymous letter saying that both in the capital and in the provinces there were dissaffected persons and that dangerous conspirators were afoot, was read out.

'What did you mean by those lines?'

'I can't mention any particular names,' replied Lilliehorn, evasively. 'I suppose I must have heard many people giving vent to their dissatisfaction. But who they were – no, I don't remember. Nor could I ever prove it.'

'And the conspiracies?' It was Liljensparre who put the question.

'I know of no conspiracies. If I wrote that, it was to make the king pay more heed.'

'You have heard people express their dissatisfaction. With which of the king's measures have they been dissatisfied?'

'I crave your indulgence, gentlemen, the expression was perhaps too strong. But my intention was honourable. Never for a moment have I wished to belittle His Majesty's many brilliant qualities or his great achievements.'

In a voice trembling with emotion the guards officer again affirmed his confidence in his former benefactor. But Liljensparre gave him no respite.

'That *billet* you received last Friday, can you produce it?'

'No, I tore it up and threw it away after I'd written my own letter, for fear of its being seen in my hands. I realize now it would have been more circumspect to have kept it.'

'Are you acquainted with Anckarström?'

'As an honest man, I can't deny it. He has twice been in my house, to see if there were any rooms to rent. And eight or ten days ago I met him at a dinner at Captain Gyllencreutz's. I have no memory of him inveighing against the king.'

The Public Prosecutor suggested that the president should ask the lieutenant-colonel whether he had told anyone about his letter.

'Not last Friday,' said Lilliehorn. 'But yesterday morning, when Bror Cederström and I were leaving the Palace, he asked me to tell him on my word of honour whether I'd written it. And I admitted I had.'

'But when the baker's boy came to get his money, it suited you better to deny it?'

'I didn't want to be found out.'

'Can you describe that other lad, the first one, and say what time it was he came?'

'It was just after six o'clock,' Lilliehorn's reply came back. But then he had to ponder a while. 'Mostly, I thought he looked like a beggar. His shoes were out-at-heels and his clothes so ragged and dirty you couldn't see what colour they were.'

That this boy should have been swallowed up by the earth did not sound particularly convincing. Clearly, the lieutenant-colonel could have called out through his window to the sentry to stop him. But the court accepted his explanation. A long queue of witnesses was waiting to be examined. The royal equerry, von Essen, and Captain Pollet both gave evidence about the black dominoes at the Opera. And the swordsmith, the pistol-maker, the merchant skipper and the court trumpeter all contributed their mites.

Liljensparre groaned. They were merely repeating facts he had already squeezed out of them. At such a snail's pace the matter wouldn't be unravelled in a year and a day. This simply couldn't be allowed to go on.

He went up to the Palace. To relieve himself of the burdens of government, the king – after much hesitation – had placed Duke Charles at the head of a temporary regency, in which Wachtmeister, Taube, Oxenstierna, Armfelt were councillors of state and Håkansson, the minister of finance, held limited portfolio. The Council verbally agreed to the Chief of Police's request. From now on, suspected persons were to be interrogated at the City Governor's office, the transcript was to be sent to the office of the Chancellor of Justice, and the case finally settled in the Court of Appeal. Liljensparre was given a free hand to arrest anyone he wished. His powers were almost unprecedented.

Pechlin's league of conspirators now realised the police were on their tracks, and they were growing more and more anxious for every hour that passed. Johan von Engeström consulted Nordell as to how, if summoned for interrogation, they could best explain their nocturnal promenade. What about saying the mild weather had been favourable for taking walks? At his evening meal he met Bielke. The baron was all on edge. That letter he had written to his son-in-law was still giving him no rest. He was sure it must have been opened by the Chief of Police. Bielke sounded so miserable and was so tedious about it all that Engeström began to pull his leg.

'It's easy for you to laugh,' groaned Bielke. 'You who don't know all the details. Let me tell you about them.'

'Not a word.'

Engeström turned his back on the despondent Bielke. In these circles it was best to know as little as possible. Already he knew too much.

The town was asleep in the dark March night when Liljensparre, firmly determined to obtain his confessions, struck. At ten o'clock Horn was fetched to the police office. In his gentlest voice the Chief of Police began to interrogate him.

'Yesterday, Count, you said the domino costume now out at Huvudsta is your own. But today Anckarström has told me he hired it for you from a shop.'

Horn did not reply.

'It is equally untrue that you are always armed on your journeys in and out of town from your country place. On many occasions you have made this short journey unarmed.'

No answer.

'And the overcoat found in his room; that's yours, too. You changed your clothes there for the masquerade. I am beginning to entertain serious suspicions, Count Horn, that you are in the plot.'

'Since I have been treated with both kindness and gentleness,' Horn began, in a faintly condescending tone, 'I will answer frankly. It is true I met Anckarström in the evening and left my overcoat at his place. But is it so strange I should have tried to conceal the fact? Who wants to be mixed up in such a horrible business? We had agreed long ago, he and I, to go to the masquerade together.'

While putting on their square-toed boots and donning their dominoes, however, he had never seen Anckarström arm himself with any pistol.

'But you must have!' exclaimed Liljensparre.

'Perhaps he did it during the few moments I was down in the privy.'

Afterwards they had gone to Norrmalmstorg, and among the heaps of stones on the little road between the Princess's Palace and the guardhouse he had hidden the sabre.

'That sounds suspicious.'

Horn laughed.

'As I told you yesterday, I had other plans and didn't know how late I might get home. I might need my sabre.'

'Where were you when the king was wounded?'

'I was standing ten yards away, peeping behind a girl's mask, when I heard the shot. I tried to dash to the spot, but was prevented by the crowd.'

All this while the Chancellor of Justice, Låstbom, had been sitting there, listening in on the interrogation. He and Liljensparre were not on the best of terms, but he could not deny the latter's shrewdness as an interrogator. Again and again Liljensparre put insidious questions about the sabre and the overcoat.

One witness after another was called in to confront Horn. Gustaf Anckarström had a nasty moment.

'Count Horn has just admitted that the overcoat is his,' said Liljensparre.

'I admit it.' The major gave a sigh of relief. So that nasty little intrigue was done with.

'The count has also said that it was he and Miss Linnerhjelm who prevailed upon you to say it was yours.'

'Never! No one tried to argue me into anything!'

'Yes, we did!' shouted Horn.

'I don't know anything about that,' protested the major. 'The women in the room must have made it up.'

'If you go on denying it,' cried Horn, 'it will lead to

trouble between you and me!'

The severely compromised nobleman was threatening a duel – as if he were free to step out into the street whenever he chose.

The major muttered something to the effect that in his confusion he must have made some such promise. Other witnesses were called in. The goldsmith's apprentice had seen Horn come running down Stora Vattugränden alley, apparently on his way out of town.

'I wasn't running at all. And I wasn't on my way out of town. I was coming into town!'

Wherever he discerned a weak point in his adversary's case, Claes Horn made his lunges. Hours passed, but though cabbies, footmen and servant maids were piling up boulders in his path, he never gave up. At last, taken off his guard, he described how, at their afternoon meeting, Ribbing and Anckarström had shown him his black domino and square-toed boots, and how afterwards he had searched for Ribbing in the theatre. This was enough. A captain and a procurator were sent to fetch Ribbing, and at the same time bring his cousin and room-mate, Knut Kurck. Likewise Funck, the man who had lent him the sabre.

The time was now two o'clock in the morning; the Chancellor of Justice, overcome by fatigue, went off home. But the Chief of Police, ignoring his procurators' and policemen's remarks about the lateness of the hour, was indefatigable. Ribbing came. Arrogant and haughty as ever, his bushy hair, cut in revolutionary style, hung down round his brow.

Liljensparre requested an account of his actions in the Opera House. Would he please describe his movements.

'I arrived at the theatre, masked, shortly before twelve, and took a turn round with my cousin Kurck. As I was standing in the middle of the auditorium I heard a little explosion, and was told the king had been wounded.'

Ribbing denied that Anckarström and Horn had paid him a

visit on Friday afternoon; but being confronted with his friend, had to admit it.

'You are familiar, Count, with Anckarström's violent and bad-tempered disposition, for which he was famous in the guards. Did he speak ill of the king or the government?'

'Not that I ever heard,' averred Ribbing.

All night long the interrogation of the two counts, and of Kurck and Funck, went on. But neither Horn nor Ribbing could be induced to confess to any crime.

Morning came. Servants were already pumping water at the well in the middle of the great market place when Liljensparre at last broke off his interrogation. It was quite obvious to him that the two counts and Anckarström constituted a sort of three-link chain. If he was to break this chain, his blows must be aimed at its weakest link. Not daring to fetch Anckarström up to the police office from the guard-room in broad daylight, he hired a couple of carriages, and taking Anckarström's accomplices with him, drove over to the King's House, where the court was holding its sessions. A lock-up was arranged next door in the evacuated offices of the Court of Audits. For his own greater convenience he had the secretarial office of the court turned into a police office – in this way he would have his prisoners always at hand.

Rubbing the weariness out of his bloodshot eyes, Liljensparre went in to Anckarström. Manacled hand and foot, he was lying in a comfortless posture on his bunk. At times during the night angry words had been bandied to and fro between them. Now Liljensparre decided to go to work more gently.

'I've been in your home, Captain, and I've seen your children,' he said. 'You have lovely children. Very lovely. They asked me to bring their greetings to their unhappy father. I do so now.'

Liljensparre saw tears come to Anckarström's eyes. In the same low voice he went on:

'All night I've been interrogating the counts; and particularly from what Count Horn has to say, I realize there has been a plot. Tell me everything, Captain Anckarström. Do it for the sake of your own conscience, and for the sake of your wife's and children's tears.'

Anckarström broke down and wept. He had difficulty in speaking. His words came in spasms:

'I'm so upset by the thought of my wife . . . and my beloved children . . . ' he apologized.

Liljensparre promised to look after his family. If the captain would only make a clean breast of everything, he would even allow the children to come and embrace their father. Furthermore, he would spare them the pain of seeing him in handcuffs and manacles.

Anckarström wept still more profusely. He begged a respite to calm his distraught emotions:

'Of course Horn and Ribbing are in it!'

This was the confession which Liljensparre, hour after hour, had been waiting for. Anckarström's tongue was loosed. He gave a circumstantial account of all the past months' preparations, from that autumn day when he had first met Horn and then Ribbing, and how they had made their first tentative attempts out at Haga, at the theatre, and in the Opera House. To Liljensparre, that student of human nature, it seemed an honest confession and Anckarström's remorse sincere. But their plans for a revolution? What did he know about them?

'Of them I know nothing. All I can say is that Count Ribbing was reckoning on the support of some military units, who were to carry out a revolution.'

'What was the gist of their plans?'

'The Crown Prince was to be put on the throne. Some generals, who might be expected to resist, were to have been arrested. But I never wanted to listen when such matters were being discussed.'

It was easy, Liljensparre thought to himself, to figure out

which generals were meant. Armfelt, in the first place. And Klingspor. He gave not the slightest sign that this information came to him as a surprise.

'I know a good deal about that scheme,' he lied. 'The counts have already mentioned it.'

So far they had been alone together in the room. Now the Chief of Police called for paper, pen and ink. For the rest of the interrogation his best weapon would be a written confession. Some hours later he had the notary read it out to Horn. The count flew into a violent rage:

'What an unparalleled peice of villainy to try to make me his fellow-criminal! Is this how he thanks me for looking after his children? Certainly I've often heard him complain of being unjustly treated; but for my part, I have never entertained the least thought of murdering, stabbing or shooting the king. *C'est un horreur*!'

The hothead was not so easily broken; but Liljensparre was more than content with his victories of the night. Head high, like a conqueror, he went up the Palace stairs to report to Lord Chancellor Wachtmeister.

The rumour of the night's arrests made that Monday a day of terror. No longer could the attempted assassination be represented as the blind deed of a fanatic. Anckarström was only a tool – a tool in the hands of a league of aristocrats, who had planned – perhaps were still planning – to overthrow society. Behind the hotheads, certainly, were older, more experienced men. Those most loyal to the king cleverly fanned the growing indignation. They spoke of old Count Fersen, the grey-headed opposition leader, quietly in retirement in his palace. But these were only suspicions. There was no evidence against him, so he was not disturbed. Things went worse for General Fredrik Horn, father of one of the arrested men.

His troubles started in the morning, when some policemen came to the house in Klara Södra Kyrkogardsgata to look for compromising papers in the room his son used to stay in when in town. A crowd of the curious gathered out in the street. Soon threats began to be muttered. Though dispersed by the town watch, they came back in the afternoon. Prentices, harridans who rowed the town's ferries, carters' men appeared out of alleyways. Even respectable fur-coated burghers were not above mixing with the populace. Obscenities echoed among the houses. Gravel and dirt were thrown, followed by stones. Windows were smashed. Passions had begun to rise. In the narrow crowded street the two prosperous brewers, Abraham and Isaac Westman, and de Broen, one of the king's actors, a man who always enjoyed a mélée, were going about inciting the mob. The government posted some sentries; but this only led the crowd to believe the general must be under house arrest, inflaming it still further. The uproar grew. Now the mob was threatening to storm the general's house.

Though Duke Charles and his advisers were afraid the mob might set on the aged general, it was not until late in the afternoon that they dared to come to his rescue. Escorted by light dragoons, General von Horn was driven by Armfelt up to the Palace, in a royal coach, and there given sanctuary. A screaming mob followed the coach, and lookers-on, watching from their windows, thought they could see General Armfelt, inside the coach, wave to the mob to follow after. 'He's trying to incite the mob against the aristocracy,' they thought.

The king was lying in bed, pretending to sleep. Suddenly he opened his eyes. The distant roar of the mob, which by now had reached the bridge at Mynttorget, could be heard in the State Bedchamber. The king was obviously very much disturbed, and listened tensely.

'What's that, Elis?' he asked his favourite.

Schroderheim got up and, crossing the soft carpets which

covered the entire floor, went over to the window.

'It's the wind, Your Majesty,' he said, 'howling in the chimney.'

Grasping the handle of the damper, he went on rattling it until the yells of the mob had been swallowed up among the walls of houses in Västerlånggatan. Then he went over to the king.

'Do you know,' the king asked, 'that Lilliehorn has been drawing a pension from my privy purse?'

Schröderheim shrugged and kissed his hand.

'Well, I wish to forgive and so I will. What are Pontus Lilliehorn's brothers saying?'

'They are deeply upset,' said Schröderheim.

'You are to assure them of my pardon. No suspicion has fallen on them.'

Schröderheim tried to divert the conversation from this sad topic. But the king wasn't listening.

'What does Count Fredrik Horn say?'

'Your Majesty can easily imagine his grief and how deep must be the old man's agitation.'

'Arrested?'

'No.'

The king seemed almost afraid to go on asking questions.

'Is he arrested, or under observation?'

'Forgive my chance use of the unfortunate word 'agitation'. I am sure the aged gentleman has known absolutely nothing about what his son has done.'

'That pleases me, Elis.'

It was five o'clock, and the doctors came in to examine the wound and change bandages. This was done regularly morning and evening. While being treated, the king always sat in his armchair. Almost never did he complain of the pain. All that evening and all night the Duke stayed in the dining room. Rumours were flying about. New disturbances were to be expected. At street corners the government had posted up proclamations ordering the king's subjects not to gather in crowds, but patiently to await the outcome of the interrogations. Still more fearsome rumours were afoot. The revolutionaries, it was alleged, were planning to cause fires on the south side of the city, on Kungsholmen and in Ladugårdslandet, and under cover of this triple diversion strike and seize power. Some people said the banner of revolution had already been raised at Karlskrona, the naval base in the south of Sweden . . .

Night fell; but in the tower of the Great Church of St Nicholas no watchman blew on his horn. Instead, the alleys echoed with the tramp of armed patrols. In the State Bedchamber, in front of the tapestry screen about the bed, a little paper lantern was burning. It was all the light the king could stand, and it threw sinister shadows in the great room with its white figured ceiling. On one of the columns opposite the bed hung the king's night clock. Each time he awoke out of his slumber he kept asking the time, even though he could see it perfectly well for himself.

The chill in the room was awful. The chimney damper had got stuck. The gentlemen of the chamber, the page and the lackeys who had to be in there all the time, shivered and froze. Snatching their opportunity whenever they thought the king had dropped off to sleep, they wrapped themselves up in some furs that lay behind a table in one corner.

But day and night meant nothing to Liljensparre. Without even giving himself time to eat, he went on trying to force a confession out of Lilliehorn, Ribbing and Horn and make them betray their accomplices. In vain. To Ribbing he said:

'There was something strange about your face when you were let out from the masquerade.'

'You may know a lot about physiognomy,' Ribbing snapped back, 'but that proves nothing.'

Brought face to face with Anckarström, Horn was told in detail of his confession. Wasn't that how it had all happened?

'Can't I be spared the trouble of saying 'no' when the question is put to me for the hundredth time?' Horn hissed back.

Anckarström persisted that he had bought his pistols from Horn.

'I suppose in the end you'll be saying it was I who shot the king?' the count mocked him.

Lilliehorn, too, was questioned.

'Why, in your letter, did you warn the king to postpone the masquerade until after the holidays?'

'Mamsell Arfwidsson had told me that if the *riksdag* ended before the beginning of March, all would go well, but that this month, for the king, would be fatal,' replied the lieutenant-colonel.

Since Friday night no one had been permitted to leave the city; but before long the peasants who brought the citizens their supplies of food would have to go back to their farms and animals. On Tuesday, therefore, permission was at last granted for them to do so. Between seven in the morning and two in the afternoon they – but no one else – were permitted, after being thoroughly searched, to pass through the barriers. Liliestråle got hold of a peasant bound for Barkarby. Dressing up as a peasant himself, he succeeded – after being carelessly searched – in getting out through the barrier and went off to his parents' home at Säby Manor.

It was in the nick of time. For now the mass-arrests had begun. Liljensparre had been given a free hand, and Teuchler, his much detested procurator, was getting down to work. Lieutenant Dohna was one of the men arrested – he had taken part in the dinner at Huvudsta the previous Thursday. Another was the wealthy wholsesaler Björkman, accused of having lent the conspirators a large sum of money. All officers who had had the least contact with Anckarström, too, were being locked up. Soon forty of them were under arrest.

At Adjutant-General Klingspor's insistence, live ammunition was distributed to all the Stockholm regiments, a measure which had oddly enough been so far overlooked. All military stores were placed under guard. Cannon were hauled out to the customs barriers and anyone walking through the streets after dark was required to carry a lantern. All airholes to cellars were to be bricked up.

In the city council chamber, on Riddarhustorget, all was as usual. Goosequills were being sharpened and dipped in ink, and sand sprinkled over the folio sheets. Office personnel were arranging the documents in proper order and handing them to their superiors. But here, too, despite the apparent calm, anxiety reigned.

Hochschild, a permanent under-secretary of state, was one of those who had been deeply disturbed by the attempt on the king's life, and felt deeply depressed during the days which had followed. Now, on the morning of Wednesday, 21 March, Enhörning, one of his clerks, asked to have a word with him in private.

'What have you got to say to me?' asked Hochschild, surprised at the other's anxious looks. For many years Enhörning had given industrious and capable service in the office. Followed by the other, Hochschild went into the inner room. Just as he was closing the door, Hochschild said:

'No, don't close it. It will draw unnecessary attention.'

Standing at the window, Enhörning said in a low voice:

'The grief which I see has been tormenting you ever since last Saturday and your words to me then have lain so heavy on my conscience that I've decided to tell you what I know. It is not particularly criminal, I suppose; but troublesome enough, even so.'

'What in God's name are you thinking of telling me?' exclaimed Hochschild, backing several paces. 'Don't you think I'm already sufficiently upset without your plaguing me with your confidences?'

Enhörning, ignoring his objections, went on in a controlled tone of voice:

'Last Friday I went to Councillor Alegren, who had promised to repay a loan. He did not do so, however. Instead, he invited me to go to the masquerade with him that evening. Something special was to happen. My curiosity was aroused, so later that evening I returned to him; but as we were walking along together, Alegren suddenly said he didn't feel like it. I could go on my own, he said, and tell him afterwards what had happened. He would wait for me at Baron Bielke's. I went to the Opera Cellar, intending to see the masquerade afterwards from one of the boxes; but while I was sitting there in the Opera Cellar we heard to our horror that the king had been shot. As soon as the doors were opened, I hurried to Baron Bielke's, where I found Councillor Alegren. I told him all that had happened. Then each of us went home.'

'Is that really all you know?' demanded Hochschild, sternly.

'Yes. At first I thought it all quite innocent, but I've been so upset by what has happened that I just had to tell someone. I think Lord Chancellor Wachtmeister knows who I am.'

'All this is horrible, monstrous!' exclaimed Hochschild, and went out into the council chamber. After standing there a while, he took his hat and coat and left the city hall.

Hochschild was even more upset by what Enhörning had told him than he had cared to admit. He too had been highly critical of Gustaf III for the troubles he had brought upon the kingdom. An egoist-king, he called him, in every sense of the words. In Lilliehorn Hochschild had found a kindred spirit, with whom he could share these oppositional thoughts, and he had been paying him visits almost daily. Now, on account of that friendship, he was himself in grave danger of being suspected. In such a situation it would be best to take the bull by the horns.

Going up to the Palace, Hochschild obtained an audience

with the Lord Chancellor, who listened carefully to all he had to say. Afterwards, in one of the rooms there, he happened to run into Ahlman, the Vice-Governor of Stockholm, and told him all about it, too. Back at the city hall, Hochschild summoned Enhörning and told him he must prepare to be questioned. It would be in his interest to stick to the truth.

Shortly afterwards the detested procurator Teuchler arrived. Arresting Enhörning, he put him in the Kastenhof prison on Norrmalmstorg, in some cold ground-floor rooms on the inner side of the courtyard. The same fate befell Alegren, whom Enhörning, by his tale-telling, had betrayed.

IX

VOILÀ! ENFIN UN HOMME

During these days of terror the scenery kept shifting in the most theatrical manner. People who above all wanted to vanish without trace and who had been flitting about in the darkness of the wings would suddenly find themselves hauled before the footlights. Who could fathom the distracted state of mind behind their actions? The day now dawning – it was Thursday, 22 March – was to be Baron Thure Stensson Bielke's day.

Councillor Alegren and the clerk Enhörning now being under arrest, Bielke had been informed the previous evening that he too must expect to be interrogated. It was this that brought him to his fateful decision. Some hours were to pass, however, before he implemented it. His servant, Johan Lundquist, usually passed the nights on the floor in a screened-off corner of his master's room. That night he was told to find somewhere else to sleep, and found it among the tailors' apprentices, down in the basement. At seven o'clock in the morning he went upstairs to make up his master's fire, and found the door bolted.

'Is that you, Johan?' he heard the baron ask. 'You can come back later. I feel like another hour's sleep.'

The servant went away and came back at the appointed hour. The door was still locked.

'Go and have your breakfast,' his master called out to him. 'You needn't be back until ten.'

Bielke lay in bed listening to his retreating footsteps.

The time had come. There was no going back. Before the hour was out, he, too, would be fetched to the police station and exposed to Liljensparre's cunning questions. What had Alegren said? Or Enhörning? Had they been staunch? Had they denied all knowledge of the plans to murder the king? Even if they had not let his name pass their lips, there was still that compromising letter to his son-in-law. Naturally, the police had it in their possession. Had not all outgoing provincial mail been impounded after the dreadful deed?

Someone knocked at the door. Schmiterlöf, of course; the tailor's servant maid. Bringing him his coffee, as usual.

'No, Suzanna,' Bielke called out to her through the closed door. 'I don't want any coffee today.'

The girl went away. Bielke got out of bed and took the few steps across the room to his chest, where he kept his jars of *Cremor Tartari* and other medicines. But now it was not these he was after. It was the glass jar with the white powder. Two teaspoonfuls, he had heard, should be enough. Swallowing them in a glass of water and unlocking the door, he went back to bed.

Bielke was a great admirer of the noble Greek and Latin authors. They had preferred death to chains. That was how Cato from Utica had acted; and successive centuries had praised him for his virtue. No matter how horrible the torments, they were nothing to the shame of being forced by weakness to betray one's friends.

But suddenly he fell into a panic. Sweat broke out on his brow; and when Ödman, assistant janitor in one of the town's offices, whose daily habit it was to run errands for him, knocked at the door, it came as a relief.

'I'm so ill, Ödman,' Bielke groaned. 'Do you know the dean, on Kungsholmen?'

'Doctor Lehnberg?'

'Yes. The court chaplain. Ask him to hurry over and bring me the sacraments.'

The janitor was astounded. Only yesterday the baron had been in perfect health. How could he suddenly be in such desperate straits? But he set off at a run.

The tailor's apprentices, busy with their needles in the cutting room, saw him flying down the alley.

'No trip home to the country for you today, either, Johan,' said one of them.

'It certainly doesn't look that way,' the baron's servant admitted. Having nothing to do, he was sitting there on a bench. 'First it's last week the baron decides we're off. But every blessed day he's put it off. Then comes the nasty business with the king, and all the barriers are closed. On Monday the baron sends me to get him a passport and orders horses on Packartorget for four o'clock. And an umbrella I was to get, too. And six packs of cards.'

'Six packs of cards! Why, is he all that fond of cards, then?' asked one of the apprentices, laughing.

'Bielke's played away every penny he ever had, so they say,' the master tailor, sitting cross-legged on his table, informed them. 'And he has no occupation. He may be a baron, but he's as poor as a church mouse. Though he did pay me the rent yesterday.'

At about eleven, Court Chaplain Magnus Lehnberg arrived on the scene. He had brought with him a young lad carrying the sacraments in a case. Telling the boys to wait outside on the stairs, he sat down on a chair by the bed.

'How are things with you, baron?'

'I've been ill for two or three days,' said Bielke. 'I fancy I must have a stomach inflammation.'

'Haven't you called a doctor?'

'No, I prefer to be my own *medicus*. All I've taken is *Cremor Tartari*.'

'*Cremor* can't do you any harm; but it isn't enough. Let me call an experienced doctor, won't you?'

'It's too late.' Bielke wiped the sweat from his brow with the palm of his hand. Then, swallowing once or twice, went on in a voice hardly above a whisper. 'Tell me, sir, is it not the absolute duty of a priest, under all circumstances, to remain silent about such matters as are confided to him?'

'It is.'

'Then I will confess to you, sir, that I, together with a number of others, have been involved in a plot to free the country from this man and his strange mode of government. But now . . . now that the plot has failed, I've taken poison.'

'Poison!'

'Yes. Out of despair for our cause, and fear that if I'm arrested I may be tortured into betraying others into misfortune, without helping anyone.'

Magnus Lehnberg had jumped up from his chair. He was profoundly shocked.

'But baron,' he cried, 'how could you join so monstrous a plot? Or choose so desperate a death?'

The pains came on; tears filled Bielke's eyes.

'Our intentions were not wicked, doctor. It was love of freedom which drove me to the former. And necessity to the latter.'

'And what do you think, baron, that I, as a clergyman, can do in such a situation?'

'I wish to unburden my conscience and receive the Lord's sacraments.'

'In that case, baron, not only must you sincerely regret your misdeed, you must also disclose the circumstances.'

'May God forgive me this fault, as all others.'

Magnus Lehnberg was the country's most brilliant orator. His monographs in honour of the heroes of antiquity had even placed him on one of the eighteen blue satin chairs of Gustaf III's Academy. Imploringly he pointed out that next to God nothing was more sacred to a man than his monarch, and no misdeed therefore worse than to use violence against his precious person.

'It was not I who was to do the deed,' said Thure Bielke.

Magnus Lehnberg adjured him to reveal everything. Though some of the malefactors had already been arrested, the threat to the state had still not been averted. If revolt should flare up, it could set the whole nation alight. It was his duty to reveal his accomplices.

'Do not require anything so low of me,' was Bielke's bitter reply.

The court chaplain was in a frightful predicament. Beside him on the floor stood the case containing the sacraments. But conscience forbade him to administer them before the dying man had shown evidence of a deeply contrite heart. The sick man, God be praised, was no longer demanding the sacraments. But had he the right to prevent a fellow human being from attaining salvation? Hoping to prolong Bielke's life, the clergyman asked to be allowed to summon a doctor. After some objections Bielke agreed.

Lehnberg hurried downstairs. The door to the tailor's cutting room was standing open, and as he went by he called out that someone must remain with the baron in his absence.

'You go up, Suzanna,' said the master tailor.

The girl went up. She fancied the baron must be asleep, but just then, in that house where every sound could be plainly heard, someone slammed a door, and he looked up quickly.

'How are you, sir?'

'I'm dreadfully ill, Suzanna.'

Suddenly the spasms of vomiting came on. She quickly handed him the chamber pot.

Failing to find a doctor, Lehnberg rushed up to the Palace and told Låstbom, the Chancellor of Justice, what was going on. Now everything happened with lightning speed. Låstbom alerted the government, which ordered Doctor Schulzenheim to go instantly to the sick man's quarters. Lehnberg himself returned in company with the Chief of Police. On the Palace stairs they happened to meet with two doctors, and took them along, too.

Liljensparre waited outside while the court chaplain and the doctors entered Bielke's room. By now sentries had been posted round the house. While on their way there in a sledge, Liljensparre and Lehnberg agreed the clergyman should be the one to try to obtain a confession. But before long the court chaplain, with tears in his eyes, came out again. All his efforts, he told Liljensparre, had been fruitless. Now Liljensparre went in; but got no answer to any of his questions. Bielke would not even admit what he had already told Lehnberg about his complicity. Just as they were putting all possible pressure on the dying man, Schulzenheim, the doctor, arrived. He found that the vomiting had already stopped; the pulse was imperceptible; the stomach swollen; and the patient's whole body bathed in a cold sweat.

'Is it nearly all over with me?' asked Bielke, who was fully in his right mind and perfectly self-composed.

Schulzenheim did not reply. If he gave Bielke no clue as to whether his life might yet be saved, he thought he might still get out of him the reason for trying to take it. Schulzenheim administered an emetic: oil and flowers of sulphur.

Lehnberg's appeals mingled with Liljensparre's threats. But since nothing could break the dying man's resolution, one after another they went their ways.

In the police office many others were waiting to be interrogated. Teuchler, the city procurator, was ordered to remain by Bielke's deathbed. At half past three Bielke died, and the news of the suicide spread through the city.

By and by it reached the ears of the British envoy, who exlaimed:

'*Voilà! Enfin un homme!*'

Now all Liljensparre's energies were being concentrated on Horn. He had found him so sensitive and easily affected, it would not be long, he hoped, before he got the count's confession. To obtain it Liljensparre was loth to resort to the 'closer confinement' – torture – of which the prisoners went in greater fear than of anything else. But there were other ways of bringing Horn to book. Liljensparre had had all the window shutters screwed down, leaving only a very faint light in the room, where he had placed no fewer than five guards. One night he had even had one of his assistants carry in some handcuffs and fling them down on the bed. But this threat, too, failed in its desired effect, and the Chief of Police changed his tactics. Now he promised the count – if only he would confess – he could have his young wife with him in the lock-up.

This was too much for Horn. After a sleepless night of torment, remorseful and miserable, he sat down to write his confession. Chiefly it was his wife who was in his thoughts. With a sensibility which was to move the judges and their assessors to tears when read out in the Svea Court of Appeal, he directed a prayer to his wife:

In every line I am about to write I shall be signing my own death-warrant. It is well-deserved. But it is not only mine; no, it is likewise thine, thou, who wast worthy of a better fate than to be bound to so vile a criminal as myself. Thou, who with thy virtue and gentleness hast made joyful my days and who even at this hour canst not divest thyself of the love thou hast ever felt for me. Alas! forgive me, ungrateful wretch! And when my confession reaches thine ears, do not curse the hour of our union . . .

Having described the course of events much as Anckarström had already done – except for the latter's harsher, clumsier phrases – his thoughts returned to his nearest and dearest:

You, tiny children, who as yet comprehend not your own misfortune, live, if Providence so pleases, so as with your tears and by loyally doing your duties as subjects and citizens to expunge your unhappy Father's memory – say with your lips and your manner of living that he was, if possible, as remorseful as he was criminal. And thou, my dearest wife, thou who canst not pluck out from your heart my image so unworthy of its sacred abode, fall down at the feet of thy King and beg him to forgive the tears thou will devote to my wretched memory. I go to suffer, not what I deserve, for my crime is greater than ever my punishment can be. Fall down before the King, beg him to give my children his blessing before he departs this life, so that I may not be punished after I am no more. – Stockholm, under arrest, on Riddarholmen, the 22nd and 23rd day of March, 1792.

Claes Fredrik Horn

That night had not been easy for Ribbing, either. All night he had walked to and fro in his dark cell. His guards, sitting there on their chairs, had been forbidden to talk either with each other or with their prisoner. As he walked up and down they followed him with their eyes. His appearance was savage. None of the prisoners had been permitted to shave, and Ribbing's beard was already wreathing his weak boyish chin. Nor were they allowed any other sharp utensils, not even a knife and fork when eating the meals served up to them from the royal kitchen.

Suddenly, Ribbing stopped to listen. A strange sound could be heard, apparently from a neighbouring cell. Ribbing clutched the back of a chair. His knuckles gleamed. Now it sounded like a soft, patient whining; now grew into a loud drawn-out, terrified howl. Ribbing met the officers' eyes. The same dreadful thought passed through their heads. An officer disobeyed orders, broke the silence.

'Torture,' he whispered, covering his eyes with his hands.

An eternity seemed to pass before those horrible sounds came to an end. Shortly afterwards the all-too-familiar footsteps of the Chief of Police were heard approaching, and the cell door was unlocked to admit him. While Horn was writing out his confession, Liljensparre thought he'd take a turn with Ribbing. Wishing to be alone with his prisoner, he signalled to the officers to go out. One of them had been drawn from a provincial regiment and, with the memory of that dreadful sound still ringing in his ears, he was only too happy to leave. He had not gone many steps down the corridor, however, before he saw a young servant opening the door to a closet. And out rushed a little dog. The dog began leaping about and jumping up at the servant.

'It was the bitch,' said the servant to the officer as he passed. 'All that unchristian howling – just because she'd got locked in!'

The officer could not suppress a smile. The Chief of Police was not such a barbarian, after all.

Horn's confession had contained one passage which had made Liljensparre prick up his ears. It had narrated how, on the afternoon of that fatal Friday, Ribbing had told Horn that General Pechlin understood it had been impossible to do anything at the masquerade which had been so poorly attended. Horn had added that this was the first time he had heard Pechlin's name mentioned in this fateful context. Was this the whole truth? Liljensparre was by no means sure. But it was something to work on. Besides, Ribbing had said something about the old politician knowing all about the preparations.

On the afternoon of 23 March, Adjutant-General Klingspor, with a sizeable escort, drove over to Blasieholmen. Pechlin had just been dining with some aristocratic guests. One was his nephew, Major Etlov Pechlin, with his countess *née* Piper. Another was a brother of Staël von Holstein, the Swedish ambassador in Paris. There were also the usual hangers-on, Plomgren and Strussenfelt. There sat Pechlin, dressed in his old grey overcoat and trousers of the same colour, his worn-out boots and a grubby neck-cloth. Just as he was rising from table, Klingspor entered the dining room:

'It is General Armfelt who honours me with a visit?' asked the old man maliciously.

'No, it's General Klingspor.'

'Oh? You were once a lieutenant in my regiment, I believe?'

'I was. And I am deeply distressed,' Klingspor went on, 'that it should be I who have been given the government's disagreeable commission to fetch you.'

Pechlin pretended to misunderstand him.

'In such troublesome days as these I can well understand the government needs my advice. Unfortunately, I have no clothes in which to appear decently dressed before the government. Nowadays I never leave my house; but perhaps it will do if I fasten on my old rapier over my greatcoat?'

'In that case, General,' came Klingspor's curt reply, 'I must require it of you.'

'What! Am I under arrest?'

'Yes.'

'And you hadn't the courage to tell me so.' Pechlin gave a mocking laugh. 'Oh my God, console yourself. I'm used to these *histoires*. If you'll be so kind as to permit me to take with me the few things I need, I will accompany you.'

Pechlin had few needs. He was not a man who cared much about how he dressed. Meanwhile, guardsmen had been posted round the house, and none of the guests, except Major Pechlin's wife, were permitted to leave. In the coach Klingspor took his seat beside the old man. A number of people had gathered and were following them, shouting. After they had gone some little way, Pechlin suddenly remembered he had forgotten to bring his beloved tobacco pipes. A dragoon was sent back to fetch them.

'This is the third time I've been arrested,' Pechlin said. 'Nothing, it seems, can ever happen in this country without me being arrested. Last time it was your brother who came for me. Am I accused of some crime this time? Or has one of the arrested malefactors named me in his tittle-tattle?'

'Baron Bielke has confessed everything,' said Klingspor.

This piece of information seemed to affect Pechlin rather unpleasantly. He could well imagine that muddle-head Thure Bielke, on his death-bed, telling tales of their conversations on Blasieholmen. Bielke was never much of a one to stick to the truth. What a miserable fellow, taking poison because he was afraid he couldn't govern his tongue! But now he was dead, and with a suicide no confrontation was possible. Pechlin quickly recovered his wonted self-possession.

'More than sixty people have been arrested,' Klingspor told him. The day's wave of arrests, it was true, had swept up a great number of artillery officers and civil servants; but the figure was an exaggeration.

'But how can the Duke and the government suspect a man of seventy-two? Can there be any Swede so low-minded as to confide plans for assassination to a man of my age? Even a Turkish dog or a barbarian would hardly do such a thing.'

'The Duke and the government,' Klingspor replied, 'are incensed that you have not personally been up to inquire after the king's health.'

The general flew into a rage. How much did they think they could expect of an old man with one foot in the grave?

'I took my leave of the king and court in '86,' he muttered. 'Since then I haven't been outside my house more than twenty-five or thirty times, and six or seven times I've caught such severe colds or suffered so from prolapsed piles, I've nearly died. Tell them that – with my humble respects!'

On its way to Riddarholmen the closed coach rolled past Arsenalsgatan.

'It's not so surprising if you are under suspicion in these dreadful times,' Klingspor said. 'General Horn has also been arrested, on suspicion. You are to be taken to the Gourt of Appeal. It has orders to meet at four o'clock.'

But General Pechlin was not taken to the Court of Appeal. He was placed under guard, like the others, in the court of audits. There, before his case came up, the all-powerful Chief of Police was intending to force him to confess. For the moment, however, Liljensparre had his hands full with Anckarström's closest accomplices. Horn had confessed. Now Ribbing must be made to open his heart to remorse and confess his complicity.

By now a whole week had gone by since the shot at the masquerade. The king's condition was not giving his four doctors any immediate anxiety. The suppuration continued, and the king received visits, both often and willingly. On Saturday morning his theatrical collaborator, Gudmund Jöran Adlerbeth, was admitted. As usual, the king was sitting in his armchair. He was pale; but his glance was lively and gay.

'Don't you think *Oedipe* was played better the second

Anckarström being flogged (*above*) and at the pillory with his weapons.

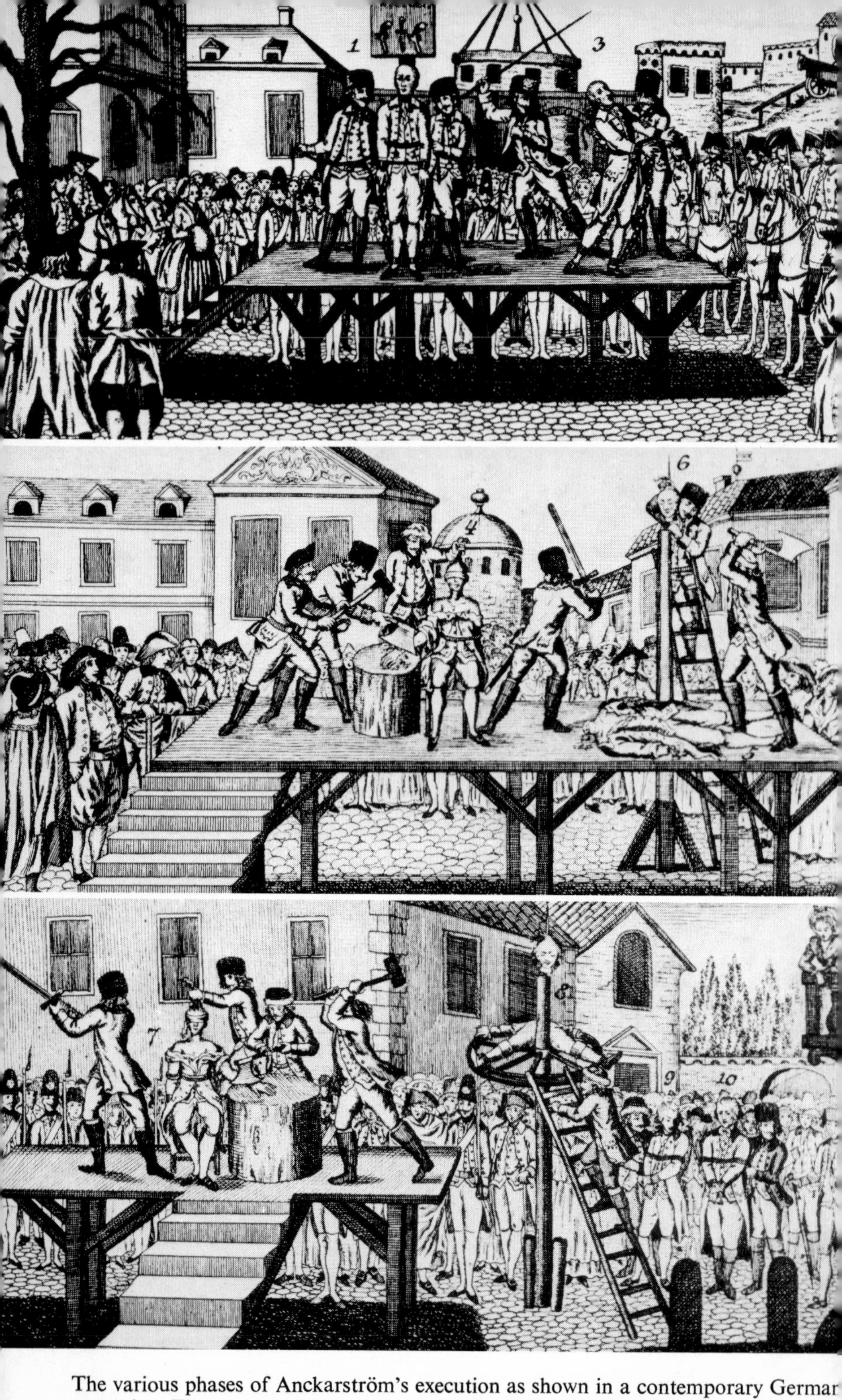

The various phases of Anckarström's execution as shown in a contemporary German engraving. The same punishment was to be expected by his accomplices.

time than the first?' he asked.

Adlerbeth was author of the tragedy which had been put on for the second time at the Bollhus Theatre the day before the masquerade. It was the last Swedish play the king was ever to see. They began a lengthy discussion on the Academy of Arts and Sciences. While they were in the middle of it, Salomon the surgeon came in and adjusted the bandage.

'Can you imagine,' the king said. 'I've had the strength of mind not to inquire about the circumstances behind what has happened to me.'

'Your Majesty has never been greater than at this hour.' said Adlerbeth, with high pathos.

'If I troubled myself about such things, my health would suffer.'

The king dozed off. Then woke up again and apologized, saying it was his food that had tired him. But those who were in attendance on him that Saturday evening thought he seemed more exhausted than before.

All that evening and night, as for so many nights previously, the lamps burned in the prisoners' house on Riddarholmen. Hour after hour, Liljensparre, with Horn's written confession in his hand, attacked Ribbing. Wasn't his name mentioned on every second page? Hadn't he been the organizer, the real driving force behind the attempt on the king's life? What was the good of persisting in his denials?

They were sitting by themselves in the dimly lit room. Here, too, the shutters had been screwed down. Sometimes Liljensparre spoke in a low voice, appealing to his prisoner. Sometimes he raised his voice, threatening other measures. Ribbing was seized with fear. He remembered the whining sounds he had heard a couple of nights ago. Towards morning his resistance snapped. He confessed. All had happened exactly as Anckarström and Horn had said.

Liljensparre gave a sigh of relief. Getting up, he went out to fetch paper and writing materials. In spite of everything –

he had to admit to himself – the count's conduct had impressed him. The ideas of human rights Ribbing had imbibed when fighting with his French friends for the freedom of the young North American Republic commanded the respect of all honest men.

As the Chief of Police came back into the cell, Ribbing came towards him. He was holding a razor in his hand. For a moment Liljensparre was quite alone with his prisoner. Was he going to murder him before he could beat a retreat? It would be a moment's work. Cold sweat broke out on his forehead. But Ribbing, with a little smile, laid down his razor on the table.

'I've had it in my pocket all along,' he said. 'No one found it when they searched me. Tonight, sir, while you have been threatening me with close confinment and torture, I have several times contemplated murdering both you and myself.'

'Really, Count? And what has hindered you?' Liljensparre asked. He was still trembling with fright.

'I consider suicide to be a despicable act of weakness. And I have felt my hands tied as if by an invisible guardian angel. Not my own guardian angel, sir, but the one that looks after you.'

At that moment Liljensparre found it hard to hide his kindly feelings for Ribbing. Indeed he felt so conciliatory that for several hours he allowed him to meet Claes Horn and his countess. He was also allowed to see his sweetheart, Lovisa Hierta.

Then he sat down to write out his confession. Someone must have told him of the great wave of arrests which was sweeping over the city.

Most deeply moved by the fate of the many innocent persons who, between hope and fear, are calling out for my confession, I take up my pen to tell of the horrible assault committed on Friday last against the king's person. An account which perhaps would never have been wrested from me by the worst torture or pains, but which my conscience and my sensible feelings for my suffering and unhappy fellow-citizens now require of me. An account with which I must and will soon appear before the eyes of the All-Seeing and the court of the All-Knowing.

I knew of Anckarström's plans. Did not avert them, did not report them. Therefore I am guilty, no longer either can or will deny it. May the fate I have deserved therefore strike me down rather soon than late. I shall endeavour to meet it with composure. My life has already lasted too long. May God grant that the days which for me are shortened may prolong those of the kindest and unhappiest of all mothers, that my conscience may, at least, not be burdened with the crime of costing the life of her to whom I owe my own . . .

This confession once in his hands, Liljensparre had Ribbing moved to a better room. His guard, like Horn's, was reduced to a single policeman, and he was given books and other things to amuse himself with. Already the indefatigable Liljensparre was busy extracting a confession from Lilliehorn, writer of the anonymous letter.

If this Sunday, from the point of view of the Chief of Police, had given promise of better things, it was bringing deep furrows to the brows of the king's four doctors. The king's condition had suddenly grown worse. Why, they could not exactly say. Perhaps an inflammation in the wound. Perhaps the chill of the sick-room. Elis Schröderheim, always the epicure, thought that something must be wrong with the food, and personally examined it.

He had been summoned about two o'clock. The king was sitting in his armchair, but Elis was terrified to hear how jerky his breathing was and how deeply he coughed. The king talked ceaselessly and kept changing the subject. Suddenly he declared he was hungry and, calling for his steward, Gruell, discussed at length what dish he might fancy.

Schröderheim, thinking all this unnecessary talk must be tiring the king, suggested that while he ate someone else could be called in to talk to him, Schröderheim. The king could just listen to their conversation. The monarch agreed.

General Klingspor was summoned, and the two men tried to conceal their anxiety beneath a forced gaiety. The king took soup, *ragoût*, and half a chicken. Everything seemed to be going well, when, to Schröderheim's dismay, he ordered an *à la glace*.

Not for several years had the king eaten this ice-cold dessert. It could signify but one thing: that he was inwardly troubled. Only in such situations did Gustaf ever eat dishes which otherwise he never touched. That was how it had been in Finland, during the war. At the Kymmene crisis he had suddenly eaten fish, which he never otherwise ate.

In the evening he fell into a fever and suffered severe pains. His own belief was that they were due to the coldness of the room; but Elis Schröderheim was in no doubt that the deterioration was due to that miserable *à la glace*.

Sunday passed and Monday came. Although it was four days since Baron Bielke's death, the Court of Appeal was devoting many of its hours to investigating the circumstances. Bielke's servant, a maid and the neighbours were all only too willing to tell everything they knew of the baron's activities during his last night and morning. Only the chief witness, the court chaplain, Magnus Lehnberg, made difficulties. The laws governing the Church of Sweden required that he remain silent as to the secret confessions of a dying man.

Mayor Fagerström, a member of the court, had no such qualms. His view was that in a case of high treason touching not only the king's person but also the security of the realm, Lehnberg was in duty bound to witness under oath. After a lengthy discussion the court decided that this was so. On his evidence Baron Bielke's guilt was fully confirmed, and the verdict on the suicide was soon passed.

Thure Stensson, formerly Baron Bielke, had forfeited his noble name and rank. Under the criminal law his dead body should be taken out to the forest and buried in unsanctified ground.

Idlers hanging about the iron railings at Slussen that Monday rubbed their eyes. What sort of a cortège was this approaching from Kornhamnstorg? The hoofs of the trotting horses rattled against the cobblestones. The advance guard must amount to a good fifty Light Dragoons, and as far as could be seen the rearguard was at least as strong. Who could be rating such magnificent honours? No golden state coach drew into sight, not even a simple cab or sledge. Yet something was glimpsed in the midst of all those blue-clad horsemen.

Good God! A sledge.

On either side policemen with halberds were trudging along. Behind came the headsman. Yet no delinquent was to be seen. Instead a corpse, wrapped in white linen, lay on the sled. The wretched Baron Bielke's dead body. He was being taken out to Skanstull barrier, to be buried on gallows hill.

Just as the miserable procession had crossed the sluice bridges and reached Götgatan, it was halted by an orderly at Postmästarebacken. He had ridden at a gallop to catch up with it. Either out of inefficiency or some misunderstanding there had been an error. The dragoons should never have formed an escort for the suicide. They were to have spread themselves about the city in half-troops to suppress any attempts at revolt by the 'patriots', which were feared.

The sled went on. Now only the headsman and his assistants honoured Thure Stensson, formerly Baron Bielke, as he made his last journey to unsanctified soil.

X

DEATH'S HARVEST

The patrols of dragoons in the streets bore witness to the government's fears. So, too, did all the arrests. They had now reached such proportions that even Liljensparre thought things were going too far. Låstbom and Vice-Governor Ahlman held the opposite view. The faintest shadow of suspicion was enough for someone to be thrown into prison, or at least to be placed under observation in his own rooms. Of the artillery officers, not only Major von Hartmansdorff and Lieutenant Ehrensvärd were in trouble, but also Colonel Gyllengranat, who had declared he would support the revolution if only he received authentic orders. In Pechlin's house, Strussenfelt, Plomgren and Hierta all had appearances against them. Why had these subalterns been so keen to attend the masquerade ball? It could certainly not be explained in terms of a mere love-sick desire to pirouette around the general's mamsell in the quadrilles. Hierta's assertion that he had been standing on the right-hand side of the stage when, on the left side, the shot had gone off, agreed badly with what little Anna Johanna Unge had to say. Nor did those night-jays, Nordell and Johan von Engeström, go free. To all appearances they had been familiar both with the assassination plans and with the revolution; and had done nothing to avert either. That was bad enough.

Lilliehorn's tales about Johan von Engeström had caused him, too, to be placed under house-arrest. He had been there for several days when, one night at about eleven o'clock, he heard a cab draw up at his door. It had come to fetch him to the Court of Audits. Two officers and a soldier were on duty in his room. All speech and tobacco-smoking were forbidden. Neckerchief, garters and knee-buckles – all were taken from him.

This was now the routine.

Now Lilliehorn, too, had been made to confess. His resistance broken, he became so talkative and so candid in his written confession that in his fall he dragged down many others with him. For Lilliehorn, the writer of the anonymous letter, his fellow-prisoners had nothing but contempt. As for Lilliehorn himself, he took consolation in religion. Singing psalms morning, noon and night, he exhorted the policemen to join in and flung his window wide open. His singing could be heard far and wide.

It was the night of 28-9 March. Suddenly the cough which had been tormenting Gustaf III ceased. The doctors realized the end must be near. His last hours, as power slipped from his hands for ever, were to be as dramatic as those other hours, twenty years ago, when he first seized it. Now there was only one question: who was to govern the realm after his death, during the Crown Prince's minority? For the imprisoned regicides and their accomplices everything hung on this question. For them, depending on who won this game, the outcome would either be certain death or hope of a milder sentence.

That night Armfelt went up to the king's bed. At either corner of the king's pillow, raising and lowering it to reduce the pressure on the inflamed wound, lackeys were standing. But Armfelt spoke to the patient in so low a voice that not even they could catch his words. Despite the eau-de-cologne repeatedly sprinkled on the bed and on those standing around, the stench was worse than ever.

The royal favourite was not displeased with his answer. What they had been talking about was the king's will, which lay in the keeping of the Svea Court of Appeal. The Lord Chancellor had been keeping an eye on it, not so much out of consideration for the king as in the interests of the Duke. In this will Gustaf III had enjoined that, after his death, the Duke should rule as regent. But in the regency during the king's sickness the Duke, like all other members of the council, Wachtmeister and Taube, Armfelt and Oxenstierna, had enjoyed only a single vote.

At half past five in the morning word was sent to the Duke to tell him that the king's condition had deteriorated. Before coming to his brother's bedside, he notified the Lord Chancellor of the situation, calling him in his letter 'a friend in whom he was glad to confide.'

The king had summoned his old doctor Dahlberg. Years ago Dahlberg cured him of a serious illness. The quartet of physicians who had until now attended upon him were not enough. Dahlberg came, and with sour looks the quartet trooped out of the room. Dahlberg gave the patient some new medicine and Gustaf's belief in its powers had such a good effect that he began talking about soon making a journey abroad.

'You can't be thinking of such a journey now,' said Dahlberg seriously. Seeing only too well how things stood with the king, he asked to be allowed to summon the Duke; in the hour of death the two brothers must be entirely reconciled. But the rumour that the Duke had been in close touch with the conspirators had reached the king's ears.

The king looked at his doctor. amazed.

'Now I understand! Am I going to die?' He struck his breast vehemently. 'Tell me honestly, am I going to die, now, immediately?'

To this Dahlberg neither could nor would reply. Once again he urged that the Duke be admitted.

'No,' said the king with equal vehemence, gripping his doctor's hand. Instead, he asked him to summon Schröderheim.

Ignorant of the role which fate had allotted him, Schröderheim was driving into town from his house in Ladugårdslandet. On the North Bridge he was met by a runner, who commanded him to hurry.

The king, with drooping head, was sitting in his armchair. At each rattling breath his chest heaved violently. His attendants were wiping away the saliva from his lips with goosequills. He gestured to Schröderheim to come inside the balustrade surrounding his armchair. He must instantly write out an important document. First, there was the question of giving Taube unlimited powers over foreign affairs: second, of making Armfelt governor plenipotentiary of Stockholm. In his last moments Gustaf tried to place more power in the hands of his favourites. But his most important act of all was to add a codicil to his will. It stipulated that after his death not the Duke alone, but the present interim government, should form a regency.

In the happy years of the reign Schröderheim had been responsible for the royal pleasures and amusements. Now he hurried out to draw up these grave deeds. He knew all about Gustaf's testament, but hastening back to the audience chamber with the papers in his hand, he found both the Duke and the Lord Chancellor already there, and showed them the documents. What should he do? Unlike Taube or Armfelt, Wachtmeister was no thoroughgoing Gustavian. He stood closer to the Duke's camp.

'Just don't go in again,' he advised.

Schröderheim was in a quandary. Like Buridan's ass with its two trusses of hay, he asked himself which was the more dangerous: to connive at wresting power from the hands of the regent appointed by the original will, or to bring down upon himself the hatred of the other Gustavians? As for his rival Armfelt, Schröderheim detested him.

'As long as the king lives, I must obey,' he groaned. But was in no hurry to return to the bedchamber.

It was Armfelt who released him from his quandary. Calling him in, he stood guard at the door to prevent the

Duke from entering.

In the sickroom Bishop Wallquist was obliged to interrupt the communion service for the king to sign the documents and the codicil. Both were hastily countersigned by Schröderheim. It was an interruption of no great consequence. Mostly the monarch's spiritual adviser had been called in for appearances' sake. The interlude over, the bishop was again permitted to hurry on with his prayers.

Time passed. Once again Schröderheim was called in. The king had another command for him. In the interim Gustaf had been put back to bed. Now he was lying with closed eyes. At Dahlberg's instigation, Schröderheim uttered his own name. All the dying man could do was squeeze his hand.

'No further answer is to be expected,' said Dahlberg.

Shortly afterwards, all was over.

The Queen, the Duchess and the Princess, all on their way to the deathbed, were checked by the Duke who, wishing to prevent them from upsetting each other, entered instead, burst into tears by the bedside, and for a long while, hands clasped, eyes turned heavenwards, stood by the doors to Charles XI's gallery. Then, again going out into the audience chamber, met his younger brother, Duke Fredrik Adolf.

'My brother,' he said. 'I bring you the most mournful tidings. The king is dead. Promise me, my brother, to defend with your life and blood that child which Providence has committed to our hands.'

Flinging himself into an armchair, the Duke gave vent to his grief, but soon got up again and went out into the dining room, where the crush was even greater. Weeping and sobbing were heard on all sides. Taube had to be carried, and Armfelt supported, out of the bedchamber. Each retired to his own dwelling. The Duke obliged all present to swear an oath of fealty and obedience to the Crown Prince, and at the same time himself swore his own oath of fidelity to the constitution and the Act of Security. To their amazement the Gustavians now noticed that among those who were willing under these altered circumstances to recognize this much-hated measure were some of its most embittered opponents – Magnus Brahe, Claes Lewenhaupt, Stierneld, Charles and Louis de Geer.

When the weeping and sobbing looked as though they were never going to come to an end, the Duke said:

'Gentlemen, our grief is reasonable; but let us remember that we are men, and abate our lamentations.'

Whereupon he sent the Lord Chancellor to the Svea Court of Appeal to fetch the royal will. Accompanied by Oxenstierna and Håkansson, he went into the Silken Room, where the provisional government had been holding its meetings. Two of its members were absent and had to be sent for. The messenger found Armfelt lying on a sofa, weeping, and Taube no less overwhelmed with grief. It was in the same distraught state of mind, utterly powerless to oppose what now happened, that they sat down at the council table.

Wachtmeister came with the will; also an envelope containing the codicil, which Schröderheim had given him. Both documents were read out. Hearing the contents of the codicil, the Duke's features darkened.

'If the codicil is to apply,' he declared, 'I will have nothing whatever to do with the government. But how is it?' he went on, pushing the sheet of paper over to the Lord Chancellor, 'Is this codicil valid under the laws of the realm?'

Wachtmeister, that friend on whom the Duke could rely, had his reply ready.

'Under the laws of the Swedish Realm, all wills must be witnessed by two persons. This is only countersigned by Secretary of State Schröderheim.'

The codicil was therefore unacceptable. The Duke said he would only obey the will which gave him royal powers. Neither Armfelt nor Taube had the presence of mind to point out that many witnesses had been present in the bedchamber when the late-lamented king had signed his name – they were altogether too broken by grief. Nor were they sufficiently versed in the law to point out that, in that law, nothing was said as to the manner of witnessing the testaments of kings.

For the prisoners the consequences of what had happened in the Silken Room, even before the king's corpse had had time to grow cold, were immediately manifest. The very same afternoon their guards were reduced and the duty officers were even permitted to speak to the prisoners, providing they didn't talk politics. Next day the Duke ordered the police office to inhibit all further investigations; contenting themselves with what had already been achieved, they were only to examine those who were already under arrest.

'I'm cutting the whole wretched skein,' he told the poet Adlerbeth. 'It's so long and tangled, no one can say where it will end.'

There was much truth in this. The threads were already leading to eminent families whom the new government would not for the world wish to offend. Not to mention certain eminent brothers of the Order of Freemasons. Some of the arrested persons had to wait to be set at liberty. But their cases never came up before the court. They were allowed to keep their official positions and the full confidence of the authorities. One of those who had been arrested for conspiratorial activities was even to be accorded the honour of bearing Gustaf's coffin at the funeral. The *volte face* was so striking that the Gustavian, af Nordin – he who had supervised the arrangements at the Gävle *riksdag* – declared: 'Many of our friends think the investigation is not being pursued with sufficient vigour.'

All round Stockholm the sentries who had been posted outside the inns were removed. Once again, everyone could pass freely in or out through the city barriers.

Where the most compromised prisoners were concerned, however, the investigation became more intense than ever. So it was for Pechlin. Liljensparre had had to sacrifice many night's sleep over the real regicides; but at least he had had his reward: their confessions. But not so with Pechlin! Pechlin denied everything. No promise of favours to his family could induce him to confess. Here all appeal to sentiment was useless.

Liljensparre countered with equal toughness. The windows of Pechlin's room were nailed up, candles were kept burning all day, his rations were reduced, and the general was awakened every ten minutes during the night. Not even when Liljensparre deprived him of his dearest earthly possession – his tobacco pipe – did it produce the desired effect. After a few days of torment he got it back – only to see it vanish again.

Worst of all was Pechlin's imperturbable good humour. He loved to talk: his speech was a trifle slurred, perhaps, but then he had so much to say. Irritated by his unceasing stream of talk, the officers on guard reminded him that all conversation was forbidden.

'In that case, gentlemen,' muttered the old man, 'you'll just have to listen.'

And then, one day, after a stormy interrogation, Pechlin, to Liljensparre's indescribable joy, asked for pen and ink. A long while he sat there, writing busily in his big shaky handwriting and carefully numbering each page. But when Liljensparre read what the old man had written, his joy turned to fury. This was no confession! It was an outrageous – if occasionally incoherent – account of the way in which he had been treated:

8th. Next day the Chief of Police came back and ordered out my guards and, as soon as they had gone, abused and scolded me and made such insimulations [*sic*] as all the fishwives of Stockholm together could not have said as much, and that, in so loud a voice, that the guards and the company outside could clearly hear it. I raised my voice as loud as his and asked him to call some of them in as witnesses, or else to keep a transcript and he would get clear answers. But he only shouted all the

louder, all over again. But I replied: Are you trying to incite the *peuple* against me again, who can prove to you that at least twice before in your presence you, against your duty and flouting both public and private safety, and without witnesses or transcript, will get no answer to all your oaths and lies; on which he flew out of the door and ordered tobacco and pipes to be removed.
9th. Next day, while I was lying on my bed, he came back again, ordered out the guards, as usual, and addressed me just as furiously, however pleasantly I pointed out to him the illegality and violence of his behaviour.

Pechlin stood his ground. He would let no paper go out of his hands without first seeing it witnessed. Obstinately he denied everything. Knew nothing. Confronted with those of his fellow-prisoners who had already made full confessions, he accused them of ganging up on him and telling a pack of lies.

Such staunchness did not fail to impress the younger officers. One day Liljensparre, to scare the old man, sent in the executioner. The headsman flung down handcuffs, girdles and chains on the floor. Pechlin just shrugged his shoulders. The duty lieutenant asked him whether he did not realize what awaited him if he did not confess.

'Well, the eye can always do with a little variety,' said Pechlin.

A certain stonemason, a member of the National Guard, Blom by name, who was sometimes set to watch over the general, did not feel the same admiration for his prisoner. In the room was a chamber-stool. When the food was brought in and Blom began to eat, the old fellow would go over to the chamber-pot and, taking his time about it, well and truly relieve himself. Old men easily become forgetful; and Pechlin almost always forgot to put the cover back. So Blom, his mouth full, had to go over and do it. It was not long before the chamber-pot was removed from the room.

The trial of Anckarström was the first to be summed up by

Fagerström, the prosecutor. His final pleading to the court on 7 April left no room for mercy. Whatever the punishment, he declared, it was only too well-merited. Regicide was the worst of all crimes; and since the law said nothing about the manner of death by which it should be expiated, it might even be asked whether Anckarström's blood was worthy to be shed on Swedish soil.

But nothing could be done about that now. In Sweden the cruel deed had been done; in Sweden it must be punished. Citing a certain clause in the criminal code, Fagerström demanded that Anckarström lose his right hand, be beheaded and broken on the wheel, and all his goods and chattels be forfeit to the crown. Yet even this did not suffice. For his hardness of heart hitherto, and to strike terror and disgust into all others, his punishment should be made yet more severe. He should be fastened by an iron collar to the pillory, and his name as a regicide be nailed to the gallows.

The accused himself listened humbly to these demands for his punishment. He did not claim to deserve anything less. Asked only that his wife and children should be saved from poverty and to have the Rev. Petrejus, rector of Maria Magdalena Parish, for his confessor.

The prosecutor was a hard-hearted gentleman. He objected strongly to Anckarström's survivors being allowed to retain any of their property. Several days later, however, when the court considered this final plea, its members showed themselves even harder-hearted. The man who had slain the king deserved punishment even more severe. There were precedents. Under an edict of 24 April, 1754, the criminal, in view of his extreme wickedness, could be condemned to stand for two hours on three successive days at the pillory in one of the town's market places, and at the termination of that period on each occasion be flogged with five pairs of birches, three blows with each pair. And that was the court's unanimous decision. He should also lose his noble rank. Already one of the assistant judges was calling him Jakob

Johan Jakobsson whenever he referred to him.

In the Supreme Court no objection was made to Anckarström's punishment being aggravated to include the three floggings. But that he should be deprived of his right to his aristocratic name, that was something it could not agree to. On the contrary. 'To its eternal dishonour and so that everyone should be familiar with it, the name Anckarström should be written into the verdict – "Jakobsson" being altogether too common.' But no innocent person need suffer disgrace. The Anckarström family was permitted to apply to the king's grace for permission to change both its name and its coat of arms; after which the former name was to be expunged from tables of the House of Nobles and all its records.

The regicide's brother, Major Anckarström, was notified to this effect by the Court of Appeal. In due course he adopted the name of Löwenström. As for the murderer's estate, the Duke, intervening, graciously permitted it to be passed on to his children.

In all probability the two counts could now look forward to the same cruel verdict. If their lives were to be saved, their relatives realized, delay was perilous. Baron Gustaf Maclean, Ribbing's mother's lover, therefore journeyed up to Stockholm. Gentleman-in-waiting to the Duchess Elisabeth Charlotta, he was in the good books of her husband, Duke Charles. But the Duke was little disposed to extend the royal mercy; nor was he really in much of a position to do so. Public opinion would not hear of any compassion being shown. And Armfelt was fanning the mood of hatred. He was spreading rumours everywhere of arson and smuggling in anonymous letters containing threats to the Duke's life – also, to throw everyone off the scent – to his own.

Perhaps they could be allowed to escape? From his prison Ribbing – he was not being so strictly guarded as before – managed to send out a plan, which was being eagerly discussed by his friends, assembled in Count Brahe's house.

But willing accomplices were hard to find. Even his cousin, Knut Kurck, who had Ribbing's reticence to thank for his own release, had his doubts.

Like many other people, Maclean had discovered the enmity which prevailed between Armfelt and Liljensparre. Falling into a dispute over one of the spectators' stands at the king's funeral, they had quarrelled violently, and Armfelt, letting his feelings get the better of him, had seized Liljensparre by the collar. But when Maclean gave the Chief of Police to understand that the Duke would not have anything against his letting Ribbing escape and further tempted him with the offer of a large bribe, he found he had gone too far:

'You've turned to the wrong man,' Liljensparre said. 'I shall redouble my precautions. No one is going to escape, even if it costs me my life.'

This attempt at bribery and corruption, however, did not in fact result in Liljensparre redoubling his precautions. Rather the contrary. The prisoners' existence grew more tolerable. They were allowed to see each other and even to receive visitors. Liljensparre even went so far as to help them write their petitions. Perhaps some banknotes were finding their way into the Chief of Police's pocket? Many thought so.

Meanwhile, the written confessions and transcripts of the interrogations were being read out to the Court of Appeal. The guilty men were repeatedly brought face to face with one another. Jakob von Engeström, who had been careful both in what he said and what he wrote during the trial, was one of the hardest to nail. He was deeply compromised – had he not drafted an entire new constitution? Yet he obstinately went on denying ever having had any discussions with Pechlin and Lilliehorn in Pechlin's bedroom as to who should form the new *conseille*. What he had been talking about, he declared, was a new chancelry – *cancellie* – surely an innocent enough topic of conversation for someone whose title was *Kansliråd* – head of chancery? Certainly the French and the Swedish word sounded much alike and might easily have been mistaken for one another.

Sometimes Fagerström, the prosecutor, would lose his temper and demand rigorous confinement for the accused. But this was something the court would not consent to.

Baron Thure Funck, too, had a close shave. It had been he who at the concert in Müller's salon that Friday evening had lent his large officer's sabre to the jittery Horn. Funck's servant, Kruus, who so disliked his master, alleged in his evidence that when the baron had come back into Müller's salon he had laughed, kicked his legs about and sung Victoire!

Konsertmeister Müller, however, came to Funck's assistance:

'The baron often mimics a French dancer whose name is Victor,' he declared. 'I seem to remember that on that evening he jumped about and kicked his legs in the air and said that was how Victor dances. I did not hear him singing 'Victoire', nor did he look particularly cheerful.'

The court had patiently to swallow many such explanations. Undeniably the Duke was right. It was a tangled web; and since its threads seemed to be endless, the court more than anything else longed to cut them short.

Pechlin had to wait a long time before his case came up. No one for a moment doubted his complicity. But it was not for the court to extract his confession. That was Liljensparre's business. And for once in his life the hot-tempered Chief of Police had to admit that he could get nowhere. In the afternoon of 14 April, at Fagerström's request, the general was fetched up from the room where he was being held. Already three extremely odd written statements had been read out in court. They had thrown Liljensparre into convulsions of rage, and the court had been no less puzzled. The wily old fox wrote about quite different matters from those they wanted to hear about.

Clad in his tattered old overcoat, his back bent, Pechlin

stumped into the courtroom. To its dismay the court saw he held in his hand yet another such screed. This too would have to be read out. It was entitled 'A most humble memorial'. And if for a moment any of the judges thought he was weakening, they were soon disabused:

May the Worshipful Royal Court of Appeal not ungraciously accept my presentation of these words, in writing. Astounded and moved to my heart's innermost depths, I cannot find words of such perspicuity as my duty requires, verbally.

Inconceivably grievous misdeeds, that have plunged our Gracious Sovereign and the whole Royal House as well as the entire realm of Sweden and its inhabitants into dismay, require, I assume, inconceivably grievous inquiries. But that I, an innocent man, should be obliged to submit to the same, causes in me the greatest amazement; the more so as I am sure that in view of my moral life only their guile and malice and nothing else can be the cause thereof. Wherefore I await my just liberation, and each moment it is delayed, inasmuch as I cannot for my Gracious Sovereign and the whole Royal House and every inhabitant of Sweden make manifest my innocence, my monstrous torments increase. Wherefore I most humbly apply to the Royal Court of Appeal that by its most just verdict of acquittal it will of its goodness thereto assist me and so terminate my innocent torments.

The court did not bother its head for a moment about the aged general's innocent torments. What it wanted was his confession. All the accounts he had submitted so far were so truncated, and so patently incredible, that there was now only one thing everyone was thirsting to hear from his lips: the whole story. The court earnestly exhorted him to stick to the truth. Had not the other criminals already confessed to having on repeated occasions been to the old intriguer's house on Blasieholmen?

'I've never talked to anyone about a revolution!' cried the general. 'Not to Count Ribbing, Lilliehorn, von Engeström, Ehrensvärd, von Hartmansdorff nor anyone else! Every word they say is untrue. They are merely accusing me to protect themselves. They would certainly have told quite different tales had they been interrogated by the Royal Court of Appeal instead of by the Governor's office, where they've been given ample opportunity to concert their lying statements.'

This was an obvious dig at the absent Chief of Police, and a bouquet of coarsest flattery to the judges and assessors. But Fagerström – Schröderheim called him the most ill-natured wretch ever to bear the name of a human being – went fiercely to the attack. Point by point he took up the general's dealings with the arrested men. Was it not true, as Ribbing had already confessed, that the general had asked him to obtain five or six lively fellows as leaders, promising for his part to collect people for the masquerade?

'Nothing but a pack of lies!' hissed Pechlin. 'The count came to me on 16 March to say goodbye. Next day he was to have gone abroad, and asked whether he couldn't have dinner at my place. We spoke of no plot. He can't possibly have said such a thing.'

The court had the corresponding passage in Ribbing's confession read out to him. Pechlin obstinately persisted in denying it.

'Point two,' Fagerström went on. 'Lieutenant-Colonel Lilliehorn has confessed that when he visited you, major-general, on Wednesday evening, and told you what Count Ribbing and the deceased Thure Stensson, formerly Baron Bielke, had said about the projected regicide, then you, major-general, said you had already been informed of it by Bielke.'

'Not a word of that is true! I swear by the living God we never spoke of any such matters. Bielke never so much as uttered the king's name. Mostly we spoke of the French Revolution, the British constitution and the way the bank had been plundered. Old Bielke was crazy, he ran about like a raving lunatic: I was positively frightened of him.'

Fagerström also brought up the story of the gleaming pistol. This was one of Pechlin's astute diversionary manoeuvres. In one of his accounts he had stated that at the masquerade of 2 March his friend Lieutenant Strussenfelt had bumped into a mask. And when Strussenfelt had turned round he had seen the gleam of a pistol close to the other person's arm. A couple of days later Pechlin had mentioned the episode to Lilliehorn.

'Then why didn't you report so important a circumstance to the proper quarters, major-general?' Fagerström challenged him.

'Report it?' replied Pechlin, sullenly. 'Didn't I do everything an honest man and a good citizen could do, when I took Lieutenant-Colonel Lilliehorn into my confidence? According to his own statement he was so entirely in the king's good graces he could go to him whenever he wished. Why should I have had any reason to suspect Lilliehorn? I thought he was an angel, Father Abraham himself. Anyway, I couldn't leave my rooms, old and infirm as I am.'

The barrage of questions went on. But not an inch did Pechlin budge from his position of total ignorance. He was innocent. He had known nothing of the plot to kill the king. Nothing about any plan for a revolution. To go on levelling such accusations at an old man whose whole life had been above reproach was simply shameful.

One cold grey day – by now it was 19 April – a high scaffold and a pole were raised on Riddarhustorget square, opposite the House of Nobles. At its top was a notice: Jakob Johan Anckarström, Regicide. The pistol and the knife too had been nailed to the pole, Liljensparre having personally fetched them from the court. All round, the Life Guards' bayonets formed a square.

Alert and erect, the miscreant came walking over from Riddarholmen. Unafraid, almost arrogant, he mounted the boards of this other shameful theatre, heard his sentence read out, and was chained to the pole by an iron collar. Over his dark blue overcoat and red waistcoat he wore a wolfskin. His head was bare. And all the while he gazed out over the enormous mass of people gathered in the square, in the streets and at windows. The site of the scaffold had been carefully selected so that he could be simultaneously seen from Stora Nygatan, Storkyrkobrinken and Myntgatan. As he stood there, Anckarström caught sight of someone drawing him at a window. Straightening his back, he turned towards the artist. 'Even after I'm dead I shall stand on the scaffold,' he said afterwards, to the clergyman Petrejus.

Gjörwell, his former guardian, was standing with his architect son Karl among the spectators. Having been asked out to a dinner of peasoup and pork – it was a Thursday, and on Thursdays all Swedes dined on peasoup and pork – he had no time to wait for the flogging; but afterwards his son told him how it had been carried out. With perfect self-composure Anckarström had hastily undressed and silently submitted to the first blows. Then he had begun to yell. And that woke up the crowd:

'Fire! Fire!' howled the mob mockingly. Each blow was followed by cheers.

Next day Gjörwell happened to have business at the Board of Commerce on Riddarholmen just at the hour when Anckarström was to be taken to the Haymarket.

'Look,' said a man, pointing to the executioner's cart standing outside the gateway to the courtyard of the King's House. 'There's his coach of honour!'

Not wishing to stand so close, Gjörwell went over to The Crown apothecary shop on Myntgatan, and attempted to mingle with the crowd. But Anckarström's gaze was everywhere. Spotting Gjörwell, he stared at him a long while. In his slouch hat, with his moustache and many weeks' growth of unshaven beard, Anckarström looked positively frightful. Going home to dinner, Gjörwell arrived at the Haymarket just in time to see the sentence being carried out. After the second lash, Anckarström began to cry out:

'Oh, forgive me, forgive!'

His voice was so tender and moving that Gjörwell went home, his knees trembling. Shortly afterwards the whole procession passed under his window. Anckarström was sitting slouched forward on a bench beside the executioner. On both sides of the cart followed a screaming and spitting mob which the escort had great difficulty in keeping at bay.

In Nytorget square, on the north side of the city, things were even worse. Most of the inhabitants of the district round St Catherine's church were seamen and factory workers who yelled and swore at the criminal. Commanded by Major Peyron, the Second Life Guards formed a square; but breaking through its ranks the mob forced its way right up to the scaffold, where it flung filth and tobacco quids at the prisoner as the lashes fell on his back, torn open for the third time. His sufferings were terrible. The screaming mob followed him all the way to Smedjegården, the prison on the north side of the city, where he was placed in the death cell.

When he heard what had happened, the Duke was indignant and sharply reprimanded Major Peyron for not seeing to it that his soldiers protected their prisoner better. But the major answered that he had been powerless, seeing it had been the regimental commander – General Armfelt himself – who had first broken ranks. Armfelt, too, received a reprimand from the Duke, and some while afterwards was relieved of his command of the Second Life Guards – the so-called Black-and-Whites. It was transferred to a brother of the arrested Lilliehorn.

As the executioner's cart rattled along Skeppsbron Quay on its way back from Nytorget, Pastor Roos was standing on the steps in front of one of the houses. He had buried Anckarström's mother-in-law, the late Mrs Löwen, and thanked God it was not going to be his duty, but that of Doctor Petrejus, to prepare the assassin for death. But when he got home he found to his horror a letter from Vice-Governor Ahlman, ordering him to go to Anckarström at Smedjegården.

Presenting himself before the Vice-Governor, Roos begged to be excused this dreadful duty. Surely it fell to the clergy of Adolf Fredrik parish, in which Smedjegården lay?

'These are the government's orders,' Ahlman said in a hard voice. 'As for Anckarström, he is neither the city's nor the country's prisoner, but the state's. So the government can designate whatever priest it likes.'

Pastor Roos had no choice. Arriving at Smedjegården about five o'clock, he was admitted to the condemned cell. It was quite a large room, with barred windows overlooking the yard. A little crucifix hung on the shorter wall, and in one corner a raised platform, from which the clergyman could preach to the condemned man. Benches stood on the floor, and on one side was a bed with a leather palliasse. Anckarström was sitting on it.

'Do you know me?'

'No,' came the cold, indifferent reply.

The clergyman reminded him of his mother-in-law's funeral in Solna churchyard.

'What errand brings you to me, then?'

'My errand is to prepare you for death.'

Anckarström flew into a rage. Getting up, he began walking to and fro in the room.

'I have cast away my body to torture and death, but my soul is my own; and I want no priest but the one in whom I have confidence. And that is Doctor Petrejus.'

If Anckarström reposed so much confidence in the rector of Maria Magdalena parish, it was not without reason. Three years before he had seen him accompany Colonel Hästesko to the scaffold. The only political prisoner to die in the reign of Gustaf III, Hästesko had been beheaded for flagrant high treason during the Finnish war. And Hästesko had met his death like a man.

'Consider that Doctor Petrejus is an old man,' said Pastor Roos in his gentle voice. 'He lives far from here. And if a man who is sick has no reason to complain if two doctors care for his body, there can be no harm in two priests caring for your soul, especially as your time is so short. If you think your soul your own, you are under a dire illusion. In whose power was your soul when you committed your cruel murder? In none other's, Captain, than that of the Prince of Darkness! If you let God's spirit awaken you and draw you out of that darkness, then your soul will be still less your own. For then it will belong to the Saviour, who suffered and died for your sake.'

They went on talking together until the guards came in and locked the prisoner's feet in shackles. These were not to be taken off again until the hour came for him to set out on his last journey. The heavy fetters caused him intense discomfort and although the guards with drawn sabres were posted in the room all round the clock, he even had to wear them at night. His fettered legs had to be stretched out straight, while his lacerated back forced him to lie on his side. It was an acute physical torment.

Pastor Roos came to him every day; sometimes also Doctor Petrejus. As he listened humbly to the clergymen's confessions of faith, Anckarström's resentment disappeared. One day, in the presence of Pastor Roos, his wife was allowed to come and say goodbye. The orders only gave her fifteen minutes, but at Pastor Roos's request the visit was extended to half an hour. Falling down before her husband she buried her face in his bosom.

'My Stava! Look up, look at me, my Stava!'

At last she met his gaze. He went on:

'Do you recognize me? No, you don't. For as I am now, you have never seen me before. Now you behold in me a child of God.'

He spoke at length to her of her future and the education of the children, consoling her with the thought that they were to be allowed to keep their fortune. His last request was for a clean white shirt to wear on the day he was to die. Then they kissed and embraced. Pastor Roos followed her home and conveyed the father's greetings to his children.

On Friday, 27 April, Anckarström awoke at five o'clock in the morning after a quiet sleep. The iron hobble was removed from his feet, a great relief. He dressed, and ate a good breakfast. Two cutlets, a bowl of milk and bread. The two clergymen had already got there before he awoke. With a pair of scissors Pastor Roos cut the fine linen cloth around his neck; it must not hinder the execution. Anckarström was wearing the same clothes he had worn on the scaffold, but instead of his boots wore shoes and white stockings. His request to be allowed to take the longer route out to Skanstull, on the far south side of the city, had been rejected. But at Pastor Roos's entreaty the Chief of Police permitted him to travel seated with his back to the horse, wearing his hat, and not have his eyes blindfolded.

At nine o'clock the door was opened and he came out and took his seat in the executioner's cart. His handcuffs were lightly fastened, so he had no difficulty in moving his hands, in which he was holding a prayerbook.

The weather being fine and sunny, if somewhat gusty, Gjörwell decided to go and see the execution. Perhaps he would not have stayed at home even if it had been cloudy and raining. Walking all the long way over stone-paved streets and sandy slopes, he got there in good time and took up his station on one of the hillocks, so as to follow the gruesome spectacle in detail. Already four hundred men from the First Life Guards – the regiment in which Anckarström himself had once served – had formed a square – facing in towards the gallows. Gjörwell saw a tall pole and four wheels, and in the middle of the square a timber scaffold, with two blocks. The doomed man was to lose his head and his right hand; or perhaps, depending on the cruelty of the proceedings, his hand first then his head.

Gjörwell did not have to wait very long. Soon the grim procession appeared. First came the two clergymen, in a hired coach. It halted where the road to the gallows turned off from the main road. There the escort of two hundred lifeguards also halted. The clergymen went up to the executioner's cart. Jumping lightly down to the ground, and with Dr Petrejus on his one side and Pastor Roos on the other, Anckarström walked the not inconsiderable distance into the square of soldiers, where the Governor of Stockholm, Armfelt, and the Chief of Police, Liljensparre, were sitting on horseback.

At the foot of the scaffold was a pile of spruce branches. All three men fell on their knees and said a prayer together. Then Anckarström got up, embraced both the clergymen, threw off his overcoat and, turning towards the sharp wind so his long hair should not blow in his face, donned a white cap. Pastor Roos helped him to tie a neckerchief over his eyes.

Quietly he lay down, with his head and hand on the two blocks. He lay quite still. Pastor Roos passed his hand over his bare neck.

'To thee is vouchsafed a crown of glory!' he said.

'Praise and honour to Thee, Lord Jesus, most inwardly,' Anckarström replied in a clear and fearless voice.

The next instant the headsman and the hangman had cloven head and hand from his body. Everyone was amazed at his courage.

A terrifying and bloody spectacle now ensued. Although the victim had once been one of his intimates, Gjörwell, otherwise so tender-hearted, could not restrain his curiosity, and stayed to watch it. For a while the corpse was left where it lay. Then the hangman and his assistants went up to it and turned it on its back, to drain off the blood. After that they went down again, to fortify themselves for their horrible task with bread and brandy. The crowd waited with greedy eyes. The taunts and curses died away. The loathsome creature's head, after all, was lying on the heap of spruce branches and his ears could no longer hear their unpleasant truths.

The hangman and his assistants got down to work. With a

big knife the hangman cut open the body from the neck to the waist and took out the heart, entrails and genitals, all of which were put into a bag and buried beneath the gallows. All clothes except the shirt were then removed. After which the corpse was chopped with an axe into four pieces and placed on the wheels – the two upper parts on the inner wheel and the two lower on the outer. Then a long and stout nail was driven through the head. After which one of the assistants climbed a ladder, and with blow after blow of his hammer affixed the head to the pole. The face had been turned towards the place of execution and the road. With its long black beard it looked ghastly. The severed hand was nailed up below it.

Glutted with the day's spectacle, the crowds swarmed through the city and its suburbs. The most criminal of the regicides had suffered the condign punishment he so richly deserved. In a few weeks time, they hoped, their promenade out to the gallows hill would be repeated in delightful spring weather. By then, of course, the anemones would have withered. But they would be able to enjoy the cowslips while they waited.

Deep in their own reflections, the two clergymen drove away down Götgatan in their hired carriage. Doctor Petrejus called to mind how it had been that early September day in Ladugårdslandet market place, when another aristocratic head had fallen to the executioner's sword.

'In the person of Colonel Hästesko,' he said in his quiet way, 'I once thought I saw a hero. But he was a child beside Anckarström.'

XI

A BROTHER'S LAST BEHEST

These hopes of soon enjoying a similar popular spectacle were not ill-founded. The day before Anckarström went to the block, Fagerström, the energetic prosecutor, had begun to sum up the case against the others. He stuck rigidly to the fourth chapter of the 1734 criminal code. It contained four paragraphs. All were relevant. In Paragraph 1 it was decreed that he who uses violence against the king or conspires against the realm, together with his accomplices, should lose his right hand, be beheaded, broken on the wheel, and his property be forfeit. This punishment could equally be meted out to him who, under Paragraph 2, had with his counsel aided and abetted such conspiracies or who, under Paragraph 3, had even known of but had failed to prevent or report them. Paragraph 4 was less severe. He who, for lack of binding evidence of the criminal's action or intent, had not reported such facts as had come to his knowledge, should be punished 'according to what could be proven concerning his crime.'

For Horn, Ribbing, Lilliehorn, Ehrensvärd, Jacob von Engeström and von Hartmansdorff the prosecutor therefore demanded the death penalty. They should also lose their noble rank. Six more heads besides Anckarström's, he insisted, would have to fall to the executioner's sword.

The others' crimes merited lighter sentences. Thure Stensson, formerly Baron Bielke, had anticipated justice; confiscation of his estate would therefore suffice. Councillor Alegren and the clerk, Enhörning, were a different matter. Enhörning had withdrawn a great deal of the evidence he had given in his first confession. His evidence had not provided the least confirmation of any criminal act on Alegren's part.

So the latter should be acquitted. As for Enhörning himself, he could be let off with a lighter sentence, for falsely accusing Alegren. As for Liliestråle, the prosecutor left his punishment to the court.

Then there was Jakob von Engeström. For his silence in not reporting what he knew of the conspiracy he deserved to lose both his noble rank and his office. Nordell, too, should at least be declared unworthy of holding public office; a severe blow to a district judge who had hitherto enjoyed everyone's confidence.

But Pechlin? What were they to do with this old general and his obstinate denials? To prove his guilt the unanimous evidence of two witnesses was required. But the evidence was insufficient. All the old fox's conversations with the conspirators of the aristocratic league had taken place one at a time, behind closed doors. At his dinner table the conversation had always turned on indifferent matters. Pechlin himself maintained he was the innocent victim of a plot by the other prisoners; and nowhere in the law of Sweden, he pointed out, was there a paragraph, even a single word, about punishment for the innocent. The prosecutor's recommendation was that the general be imprisoned in a fortress and there be exhorted by the clergy to repentance and a true account of the whole affair. Society must protect itself against his subversive activities for the future. The prosecutor had a long memory. The threads ran back.

For the prisoners on Riddarholmen the following weeks were filled with anxiety. Lilliehorn's psalmody became so persistent that Ribbing complained it was getting on his nerves. Horn and Ehrensvärd wrote poetry. And Pechlin lay on his bed, smoking his pipe. At last, on 24 May, their sentences, pronounced by the Court of Appeal and somewhat mitigated by the Supreme Court, were pronounced.

Four, not six, were condemned to death: Horn, Ribbing, Lilliehorn, Ehrensvärd. With them the law must take its course. The Lord Chancellor would have preferred to spare Ehrensvärd on account of his youth, but felt that the law must nevertheless be applied in all its rigour.

As for Pechlin, he was to be sent to a fortress. The others' final sentences were lighter than those demanded by the prosecutor. Jakob von Engeström got imprisonment for life, and Hartmansdorff – he who had promised to hold the artillery in readiness – got off with loss of his major's rank and one year's imprisonment. Alegren was wholly acquitted. Johan von Engeström, deprived of his post in the civil service, was released. For Nordell and Enhörning, too, the prison doors were opened.

'Never has an act of regicide been investigated and punished with greater leniency. Of that,' said Adlerbeth, the dramatist, who did his best to see the trial objectively, 'there can be no question.'

Small wonder the Gustavians felt bitter about it. They had hoped to see rivers of blood flow. And all over Sweden people were crying out for revenge. Popular feeling supported Armfelt, Taube, Ahlman, Låstbom and Håkansson, the most faithful – but also the most vengeful – of the late king's supporters. Even the man already executed, they thought, had got off too lightly. At the very least his accomplices should suffer the same punishment, with the pillory and floggings as a foretaste of the gruesome ceremony on gallows hill. What sort of tender-mindedness was this, imprisoning Pechlin and Jakob von Engeström in a fortress? And why such obviously lenient treatment of the Engeström brothers? Was it not due to their bosom-friendship with Baron Bonde – the Freemason who now so closely associated with the Duke, and to whose opinions the latter was always so disposed to listen? There was another gentleman in the Duke's good books: Baron Staël von Holstein, the former Swedish ambassador in Paris, husband of the literary daughter of the former French minister of finance, soon to become famous throughout

Europe as the authoress Madame de Staël. Gustaf III had removed him from his post on grounds of his excessive libertarian and republican sympathies. And there was one more, too, though he was still abroad and not expected home before about midsummer: Baron Gustaf Adolf Reuterholm, another fanatical Freemason and the Duke's closest friend. Reuterholm was another close friend of Bonde's. All that winter and spring Bonde had been keeping him informed of the latest sensational events at home in Sweden. Despite the late king's attempts on his deathbed to leave power in their hands – attempts which had been partially succesful – the Gustavians were gradually being pushed out from the centre of things. But they were still too strong to be thrown from the saddle. Popular feeling, popular hatred, were their best ally.

The court of appeal had given sentence. Not only those condemned to death but also those members of the aristocratic league who had received lighter sentences were granted thirty days' grace to lodge their appeals. This gave the vacillating Duke a breathing space. By the time the appeals came in it would be midsummer, and the members of the Supreme Court would be due for a month's holiday to enjoy a little peace and quiet in the summer countryside after so troubled a spring in town. So the Duke would have plenty of time to make up his mind. Perhaps in the last resort he would decide to let mercy come before justice? So at least Bonde and Staël von Holstein, not to mention all the relations and friends of the prisoners, were hoping. Among the latter, oddly enough, could be reckoned the Chief of Police, Liljensparre.

And indeed the Duke was in acute need of such a respite, for he had political problems of greater import on his hands, such as required a diplomatic solution. The Empress Catherine II of Russia had not forgotten Gustaf III's generous offer of ships and soldiers for a crusade against the French revolutionary government, so hated by all the crowned heads of Europe. At the end of May 1792, the Duke gave her to understand that this would be a suitable moment to send troops to Germany. About the Duke's person there were many – above all the enthusiastic crusader Taube – who thought the expenses of such a campaign might be justified, providing Russia increased her subsidies. Though the Duke did not dare to cross the redoubtable Empress, he was troubled by his late lamented brother's pact of friendship with Denmark, Sweden's hereditary enemy to the south. Swedish assistance, he declared to the Russian envoy, was dependent upon Swedish subsidies. What he was careful *not* to point out, was that no such subsidies had ever been promised. But the chief reason why he – and his advisers – wanted to extricate themselves was that the country's economy was in such a precarious state. Taube and Armfelt noticed that their views were no longer getting a hearing. The Duke had begun to adopt a francophile policy. This was a remarkable about-face: his foreign policy was beginning to resemble the very one which Pechlin and his associates had so energetically proposed. The clash between the regent and the paralysed opposition was no longer so fierce. And this should redound to the benefit of the prisoners.

In mid-June they noticed that something was in the wind. A room where they could take exercise, meet and were allowed to receive friends and relations was fitted up in their prison. They were even allowed to pay each other visits in their cells. Life was becoming easier, and when on midsummer eve Count and Countess Horn were actually permitted to throw a little party, the guests included not only Ribbing, Ehrensvärd and some ladies, but also the Chief of Police and the officer of the watch, Captain Bosin, a man to whom they had taken a particular liking. They ate and drank and enjoyed each other's company. Ehrensvärd wrote a poem in praise of Liljensparre. If friends outside were wondering who had made possible this little midsummer feast, the answer could not be in doubt:

> Friends! full well ye know
> who in these cloudy days
> has done much more than laws.

More than laws! Undeniably the matters which had fallen to Liljensparre's lot to investigate had been much graver than normally come to the cognizance of a magistrate or police chief. And now, with all desirable clarity, he had let them know their lives were no longer in danger.

Countess Horn went out to Huvudsta for a day or two. Ehrensvärd directed a hopeful prayer to her:

> Approach the throne while yet you dare,
> A throne where gentleness and mercy reign:
> Return with hope of days you yet will share
> With friend and husband dear.

During these days the prisoners' appeals and pleas for mercy were coming up before the Court of Appeal. Carefully thought out, carefully worded, they appealed eloquently to the court's humane and merciful feelings. Really, it was a shame they should only be read by pedantic jurists in the great stone house next door, where the president was insisting on the law being applied in all its severity.

Whoever first hit on the idea – the Chief of Police himself, perhaps? – it was a brilliant one. These appeals for clemency must reach the great public. For a sum of eight *riksdaler* per author, they could be printed in *Dagligt Allehanda*. At midsummer an unknown poet had already published a poem which seemed to foreshadow what was to come – or at very least had drawn renewed attention to the plight of the prisoners. As long as one's fellow-beings were weeping behind prison walls, what enlightened person could enjoy the lovely summer weather?

Ten days later the citizens of Stockholm, scanning the otherwise dry-as-dust columns of *Dagligt Allehanda*, could read Horn's and Ribbing's appeals for clemency. They were followed by Lilliehorn's, Ehrensvärd's, Hartmansdorff's and Pechlin's. Even Johan von Engeström, not satisfied with being set at liberty, was grieving over the loss of his job in the civil service and applied for the mitigation of his sentence.

Day after day people were entertained to such touching reading matter. A few paunchy citizens, smacking their lips over their ale mugs in the town's beer cellars, might swear and curse. But the ranks of the indignant had grown thinner.

At long last Baron Reuterholm, he whom the Duke had so long and eagerly been awaiting, was home again. The Duke had written to him immediately after the king's death, inviting him to return; but Reuterholm was a man of cagey disposition, and as long as the police inquiries were going on he had considered it the better part of wisdom to stay out of harm's way. On Midsummer Day he arrived in Stockholm. It was the Duke's wish that he should immediately take over the chancelry and all the duties of prime minister.

'I would sooner have chosen the block,' Reuterholm wrote to his uncle. 'To the eyes of those who are not in the know everything here looks quiet enough. But for those behind the scenes – oh my God, what a future! If I'd known how things stood before I came home, I should still be on foreign soil.'

So he declined the Duke's offer and contented himself with the presidency of the court of audits – an office vacant since Munck, that intimate of the late king, had fled from justice after his monetary forgeries had come to light. But Reuterholm was planning major changes in other matters than those normally pertaining to his department. Already he had drafted out a law restoring freedom to the press. One Sunday in July, after the decree had duly received the Duke's approval, it was read out from every pulpit in Sweden. A gospel of liberty:

'To limit freedom of expression or of the press is to underrate the human race and usurp the rights of man, which are rooted in nature.'

Censorship was to be abolished. Away with all those regulations through which the previous regime had stifled free speech! The rights of man! In General Pechlin's palace on Blasieholmen, too, Thomas Paine's pamphlet had been favourite reading matter. News that freedom of the press had been restored penetrated his prison walls, inspiring Horn to a poem in which he acclaimed the Duke as a hero, a Lucifer:

> None but virtue's thoughts be thine,
> In Unity your Welfare find.

Just now, however, unity was a commodity in short supply. It was precisely during those mid-July days, when the beautiful Swedish 'high summer' should have been bringing harmony to all men's minds, that an alarming rumour began to spread. The Gustavians, it was said, were planning a *coup d'état*. It was 12 July. That afternoon Bonde seized his pen and sat down to write to his friend Reuterholm.

He had heard the most dreadful things. At one of the Gustavian clubs, in the presence both of Låstbom and Håkansson, threats had rattled like hailstones:

'It is high time the Duke learnt to keep within bounds! If he has the impudence to show the criminals the least mercy or tries to delude the public into imagining he has the least power, we, who served our late-lamented king, will clip his wings for him. We'll teach him to know his place as regent!'

At Håkansson's house, too, people had been talking. When the Duke's power was broken, they had said, they would teach those boys not to crow so loud.

'Those boys'– that could only mean Reuterholm, Bonde and Staël von Holstein. Liljensparre, too, had complained of the Duke's excessive leniency towards his opponents. Armfelt, Ahlman, Håkansson and Låstbom, Bonde thought, should be sent packing within twenty-four hours.

Bonde was terrified, ready to flee to the country. If he was to be one of the victims, he said, then he would rather lose his life under his own roof than be *assommé* by the stones of the mob in some rented room in town. All this, he wrote, he had been told by honest folk – though he was not mentioning any names.

Reuterholm got the letter and at once sat down to write to the Duke. In covert phrases he warned him of a threatening catastrophe. The bomb must not be allowed to go off over their heads.

'May God watch over my Gracious Lord in these halcyon days, and over us all!'

The *coup* was to be made the following night, when Riddarholmen was to be stormed. Orders were therefore given for one of the cannon from the guards headquarters, – the very one, perhaps, which Pontus Lilliehorn had captured from the Russians – to be taken down to Riddarholmen Bridge and its artillerymen to post themselves in front of the gateway to the house containing the prisoners.

But there was no *coup*. Nor, presumably, had one been planned. But the point had been made. The irresolute Duke had been given something to think about. Now, at long last, he made up his mind. At last the new brooms were to make a clean sweep. And now everything happened with astounding swiftness. The Reuterholm-Bonde-von Staël trio had succeeded beyond their wildest hopes. On 15 July, to their unspeakable satisfaction, they were able to note in their diaries that Governor Armfelt had gone abroad. On 16 July, Vice-Governor Ahlman was appointed president of the court of appeal at Vasa, far away in Finland. He was succeeded by Liljensparre, who had long had his eyes on this important post. The change took effect immediately. On 16 July, too, the Duke appointed Baron Fredrik Sparre Chancellor of State, and Lars von Engeström – Jakob's and Johan's brother – was made Chancellor of the Royal Household. This meant that Taube no longer had anything to say in matters of foreign policy. On 4 August Låstbom, having already been virtually manoeuvred out of office, found it advisable to resign from his position as Chancellor of Justice; and about the same time Elis Schröderheim, to his no small disgust, found himself appointed Governor of Uppsala. Then it was Håkensson's turn: he was dismissed from the administration of the finances. And finally, not to mince matters, another Gustavian, Colonel Ruthensparre, who had been in command of the prisoners' guard, was relieved and sent to the west of Sweden to be governor of Marstrand fortress.

In two blows the Gustavians had been sent packing in every direction. And now at last, after enjoying their holiday, the learned justices could sit down in a calmer atmosphere to read the prisoners' appeals – if, that is, they hadn't already done so in *Dagligt Allehanda*. This they did most thoroughly, taking several days about it, and considering whether they should not show themselves more merciful than they had hitherto been inclined. In the end, however, they decided to stick to their earlier sentences. As for the prisoners' appeals for clemency, they were submitted to the gracious consideration of the King-in-Council.

The documents, passed to the Supreme Court, were rejected. In so criminal a case the Supreme Court could not agree to the least mercy being shown. Of the four men sentenced to death only Ehrensvärd was regarded as worthy of mercy. From his childhood up, after all, he had been Lilliehorn's ward.

As for the others, their sentences could perhaps be somewhat mitigated. Jakob von Engeström's life sentence was reduced to three years – all his days he had been an irreproachable civil servant, and a certain amount of consideration should be shown to his family. Hartmansdorff had fought in two wars and also enjoyed untarnished reputation. For him, too, three years would be enough. As for Johan von Engeström, the loss of his official position for one year would suffice. And what about Pechlin? Couldn't he be allowed to remain in his own home or reside on his estate down in Småland? Must he really be locked up in Carlsten Fortress? After all, he was only an infirm old man, with prolapsed haemorrhoids.

That was the Supreme Court's view. But the final decision lay with the Duke. Already Reuterholm had taken certain convenient measures to make it easier for him. By exhorting the judges to vote for milder sentences he had opened the path for the Duke to mitigate them still further.

The date was 15 August. To Drottningholm Palace, outside the town, the Duke had summoned his judicial council: Lord Chancellor Wachtmeister, Chancellor of State Fredrik Sparre, Count Ruuth, Baron Reuterholm, and three judges of the Supreme Court. As soon as they were seated the appeals were read out; likewise the Supreme Court's request that some of the sentences be reduced.

The Duke began to speak. He found himself, he said, in an acute crisis of conscience. Least of all, in the present case, was it his wish to evade his duty, which was to expose these vile criminals to the utmost rigours of the law: yet at the same time he must reconcile it with another – to carry out the last prayers and commands of his dying brother. On one of the last days of his life Gustaf III had in fact declared he would know no peace until the Duke had promised to spare the lives of all who had been guilty of, or accused of complicity, in the crime.

'And it is this remarkable and touching circumstance,' the Duke went on, 'such as in the eyes of posterity must ever place King Gustaf III's greatness of heart and mind in the fairest lights and do even more to immortalize his memory than his victory at Svensksund, which now forms the basis of our gracious judgement and decision. As a Christian, as a subject, as a brother, as a human being, we neither can nor ought to deviate from our dying brother's last behests. In a matter so entirely his own, it was his absolute right to show mercy. We never failed to implement his wishes while he was with us, nor shall we, his brother, in death allow this slur to be laid upon us.'

The Duke's decision was that the four doomed men – Horn, Ribbing, Lilliehorn and Ehrensvärd – should have their death-penalties commuted to eternal exile. Further than that in following his heart's native inclination towards gentleness and leniency he could not go. Nor could the others count on any alleviation of their sentences: he would implement the Supreme Court's recommendations. One change, however, he wished to make. General Pechlin should be sent to Varberg Fortress, in Halland, instead of to the fortress of Carlsten, at Marstrand. From the General's point of view it was undeniably an improvement. On the island at Marstrand he would have undoubtedly been exposed to renewed persecution at the hands of the displaced Gustavian, Ruthensparre, who had just been sent there as governor.

The Lord Chancellor listened to the Duke's remarkable speech with a deep frown. If he had had his way, not a man of them would have been reprieved or shown the least mercy. External exile! The sentence was altogether too light! Reuterholm, however, listened with pleasure. It had cost him no small labour to find a plausible formula for the Duke's judgement. He had consulted his friends, Bonde and Staël von Holstein. Bonde had every reason to feel satisfied that his friends, the Engeströms, got off so lightly.

The Council was over; and with the final judgement in his hands General Klingspor set off in his carriage at a lively trot from Drottningholm into town. There the commanders of the guards, the artillery and the navy had already been given a hint of what was in the wind. They might have to intervene. And Liljensparre, too, had posted his policemen all along the streets leading to Liljeholmen. To avoid unnecessary attention, Klingspor got out of his carriage outside his own house and went on to Riddarholmen on foot. The four exiles were called into the exercise room, and the doors were shut.

Klingspor handed the sentence to Liljensparre, who read it out.

Each went to his own room, to dress for the long journey. Klingspor came to Ehrensvärd, and took a touching farewell. At seven in the evening a cab trotted up, and together with Liljensparre and Captain Bosin, who at their own request was to accompany them to the frontier, they took their seats in it. At Liljeholmen they said goodbye to Liljensparre, their good friend and benefactor.

Later the same evening Horn and Lilliehorn, too, left their prison. They travelled separately, however, each being accompanied by an officer. Neither of the two exiled counts would travel with Lilliehorn, the man who after warning the king had betrayed so many.

Stripped of their aristocratic names, the four travelled southwards to Denmark: Claes Fredrik Fredriksson, formerly Count Horn. Adlof Ludvig Fredriksson, formerly Count Ribbing. Carl Pontus Samuelsson, formerly Lilliehorn. And Carl Fredrik Carlsson, formerly Baron Ehrensvärd.

Morning came. In *Dagligt Allehanda* everyone was reading the minutes of the council meeting. The newspaper sold like hot cakes. Everywhere in the town's squares and market-places people stood and gaped. Despite his passion for justice, they read, and against his own better judgement, the Duke had felt obliged to yield to his brother's dying wish.

The muttering swelled. Turned to bickering, to furious explosions of wrath. Sympathy blended with disappointment, and indignation with bitterness. The town's craftsmen and prentices, its servants and its ample-bosomed matrons, one and all felt they had been cheated. There were to be no more bloodthirsty spectacles! As for Gustavians, they were dumbfounded. But if their beloved king had wished in his mercy to pardon his enemies, it was hardly for them to show themselves merciless. That is to say, if he really had? Many doubted it. A few knew the truth. The Duchess Hedvig

Elisabeth Charlotta, for instance, sitting down at her elegant little writing table, wrote to the late-lamented king's sister: 'it is, as of course you must realize, nothing but a pretext'.

A threatening mob moved up towards Riddarholmen, where the regicides had so long been imprisoned. But Liljensparre's words calmed their anger and they soon dispersed. Nor was the city's calm so much as ruffled when the August night having once more fallen, carriages drove up to the prison doors to take the remaining prisoners to their respective fortresses. In one rode General Pechlin. Outside the city barriers stood one of his old friends, waiting to say adieu. To his astonishment he noticed that the general was as calm and cheerful as ever.

XII

ETERNAL EXILE

All that spring and far into the late summer the doomed men had been locked up in the court of audits, next door to the court whose judgement they so feared. Along the shores of Kungsholmen and in Långholmen's rocky crevices and across Lake Mälaren they had seen the silver birches' delicate spring greenery deepening into the rich foliage of the oaks. On brilliant summer mornings hay-boats had come sailing into town from Lovön and Svartsjölandet. How lovely had seemed to them the brief Scandinavian summer – lovely as life itself! They had been obsessed by one wish only: to be spared Anckarström's horrible fate. One day the Duke had come sailing past their prison in his yacht, and Horn had written a poem, wherein he likened himself and his fellows in misfortune to shipwrecked men, imploring the victor of the battle of Hoglund to rescue them.

Now the Duke, of his sovereign mercy, had commuted their death sentences to lifelong exile. But to men whose deed had been motivated by patriotism was not a life spent in banishment from their fatherland almost as terrible? What sort of a future could they look forward to? Under police escort they had been taken to Hälsingborg; thence had sailed across the narrow Öresund Strait; and, once more at liberty, had gone on to Copenhagen, there to be greeted with jeers and showers of stones by the mob of the Danish capital. Thence, each had by and by gone his own way. Let us therefore, finally, follow each of these men in turn and see briefly what happened to them.

First, ADOLF LUDVIG RIBBING. He had been the real instigator, the driving force behind the plot to assassinate the king. It was therefore only logical that he went on to Paris, that cauldron of revolution, where the National Convention had just declared France a republic. When, in January 1793, Louis Capet went to the scaffold, Ribbing was an eye-witness to his execution. But when he afterwards dared express his sympathy for the wretched Queen Marie Antoinette, then threatened by the same fate, he became so suspect in the eyes of the Jacobins that he felt it the better part of wisdom to flee the Terror and to go to Switzerland. There he became acquainted with the now famous Madame de Staël, wife – as we have seen – of the Swedish ambassador in Paris, Erik Magnus Staël von Holstein, and daughter of the former Minister of Finance, Necker, now also an exile. She was feverishly assisting the emigrés. But Ribbing did not stay long in Switzerland. Returning to Denmark, he was able with his mother's and her lover, Gustaf Maclean's, financial help to purchase the estate of Aldershvile, ten miles or so outside Copenhagen, where he went by the name of Fredriksson.

In 1796, however, he was again in Paris, where as Monsieur de Leuven – his mother's maiden name – he led the gay life of a bachelor. Marrying an ex-nun, Adèle Billard d'Aubigné, he lived with her on his own estate as a wine-grower in the Loire valley during the years of the Napoleonic Empire. After the abdication of Gustaf III's son, Gustaf IV, in 1808, Duke Charles permitted him to pay a month's visit to his mother, who by now, after her marriage to Maclean, was living as a widow on a farm in Bohuslän, West Sweden. It was to be the only break in his lifelong exile.

With the fall of Napoleon, Ribbing the regicide was obliged to leave France, and settled in Brussels. In 1813, on his mother's death and in the absence of any further financial help from home, he began to support himself as a journalist, writing for two newspapers, *Le Nain* and *Le Vrai Libéral*. His lively anti-legitimist articles, mostly about Scandinavian affairs, attracted so much attention that Sweden's new Crown Prince elect, the ex-marshal Bernadotte – soon to become King Karl XIV Johan – made him a gift of 3,000 florins.

But all Ribbing's appeals to be allowed to come home to Sweden proved fruitless. Not even Madame de Staël, at the time of her visit to Stockholm in 1812, was able to move the hearts of those in power. So Ribbing's wandering life went on. At the request of King Wilhelm III of Prussia, whom he had attacked in a newspaper article, he was forced to leave Belgium. Fortunately, the state of affairs was now such that he was able to go back to France, where he spent the last years of his restless life as a journalist in Paris, living there with his son after his wife's death. Ribbing died in 1843.

As for CLAES FREDRIK HORN, that tender-minded enthusiast, he too was to learn that an outlaw has no fixed abiding place in this changeable world: but his exile was to prove slightly less restless. Remaining in Denmark, he called himself Fredrik Claesson after his maternal grandmother, who came from the powerful commercial family of that name. Purchasing an estate at Skovlunde, a romantic idyll near Hirschholm, he was joined there not only by his wife and daughter (his little son remained behind for good with his grandfather) but also by his sister-in-law, Catharina Linnerhjelm, who in 1792 had been Anckarström's neighbour and played a not unimportant role during those fateful March days. The political atmosphere in Denmark was freer than it was in Sweden, and it was not long before Horn's personal charms had gained his admission to literary circles, where he began to associate with the famous poet Oehlenschläger and the literary critic Knud Lyne Rahbek. Horn's existence, indeed, might have been free of all complications had he not enjoyed so excellent a reputation as fortifications officer. In 1801, when Denmark, having joined an alliance of armed neutrality with Sweden and Russia, was being threatened by the British Navy, Horn was entrusted with the task of strengthening the country's coastal defences. To see such honours and attentions being showered on his father's murderer pleased Gustaf IV Adolf not at all and at a meeting with Crown Prince Fredrik of Denmark at Hälsingborg he expressed his displeasure. Horn was instantly sacrificed to good neighbourly relations and ordered to leave the country. Settling at Lübeck, he earned a meagre living there for some years by teaching languages.

Naturally, he had but scant sympathy for Gustaf IV Adolf. Perhaps this explains his treasonous activities in 1806, when Napoleon's troops, marching northward on their way to the Swedish possessions in Pomerania, seized Lübeck. Horn is said to have contacted Marshal Bernadotte, the French commander, and given him valuable military information.

In 1813, however, he was permitted to return to Denmark, where he became a Danish citizen and was allowed to reassume his proper name. Once again literary circles opened their doors to him, and in 1816 he published an anonymous collection of poems, *Små Skaldestycken*, and wrote for two newspapers, *Charis* and *Dagen*. But he was too restless a spirit ever to steer clear of politics. Now it was events in Norway that attracted his attention. The Swedish Crown Prince was casting eyes on that country and hoping to unite it with Sweden under a single crown. The Crown Prince was therefore exceedingly displeased when a rumour reached him that Horn had worked out a projected constitution for Norway and sent it to the Norwegian Parliament at Eidsvold. Some years later, in a letter to Lars von Engeström, the Swedish foreign minister, Horn firmly denied ever having done any such thing. Such mendacious accusations, he feared, might damage his son's career in Sweden.

The last years of his life were plagued with financial embarrassments. Horn died in 1823.

Of the four exiles, CARL FREDRIK EHRENSVÄRD was the one who might reasonably have felt the deepest resentment at the severity of his sentence. After all, he was very young, and many others much more deeply involved had got off more lightly.

Like Ribbing, Ehrensvärd at first thought of going to France, where he had plans to join the army; but the news of the bloody September massacres caused him to change his mind, and he stayed in Hamburg. There, joining a Jacobin club, he enthusiastically preached social equality and spiritual freedom. For some years he administered a friend's estate in Holstein. Then he visited France. Finally, in 1798, he returned to Denmark, where he called himself Gyllembourg, a slight modification of his mother's maiden name of Gyllenborg.

Like Horn, Ehrensvärd came into literary circles, being particularly well-received in the house of the radical writer, Peter Andreas Heiberg. He fell in love with Heiberg's wife, the refined and discreet Thomasine Buntzen, who was equally attracted by the chivalrous soul and courtly manners of the Swedish nobleman. When Heiberg got into hot water with the Danish government and had to go into exile, he left his wife behind. In 1801 Thomasine married Ehrensvärd. This marriage turned out to be very happy.

With funds collected from relatives in Sweden Ehrensvärd had purchased the estate of Ruhedal, in Sorö, Själland, and there threw himself heart and soul into agriculture. Fortunately his farm – it was heavily insured – burned down; so, with improved affairs, he settled down with his wife in Copenhagen. There he read deeply in agricultural science and statistics, and in his work *Forsøg til et Landbrugs-Bogholderi* – A Plan for an Experimental Agricultural Economy – he presented a revolutionary method of keeping statistical tables. In 1805, he would have received the Royal Danish Agricultural Association's gold medal had not Fredrik, Crown Prince Regent of Denmark, refused out of consideration for Gustaf IV Adolf of Sweden to present it to him. Ehrensvärd saved the situation by withdrawing his manuscript to make some additions. It was published three years later.

To throw a more favourable light on his part in the plot to assassinate Gustaf III he also wrote his own autobiography. It was intended for the eyes of Crown Prince Fredrik, but probably never presented to him. After the 1809 revolution in Sweden, when Gustaf IV Adolf was deposed and abdicated, Ehrensvärd sought permission to re-visit his native country. His request was turned down. By this time, however, he was on good terms with Crown Prince Fredrik of Denmark and was passionately attached to the 'Scandinavian' dream of seeing the three countries united under the sceptre of that prince. Ehrensvärd agitated for Prince Fredrik's election to the throne of Sweden – and was deeply disappointed when the choice fell on Bernadotte.

In 1813 Ehrensvärd took Danish citizenship and adopted the name Gyllembourg-Ehrensvärd. He died two years later.

Finally, CARL PONTUS LILLIEHORN. Ever since the day after the fatal shot at the masked ball, Lilliehorn had been treated with profound scorn by his comrades in adversity. Not only had he written the warning letter and betrayed the trust the conspirators had placed in him; under pressure from Liljensparre's unremitting interrogations, his own remorse and his weak character, he had gradually exposed all his friends. Thereafter his three fellow-conspirators had wished to have no more truck with him.

In Denmark their ways parted immediately. Lilliehorn's movements are not known in detail: but there is no doubt that he had to struggle with great initial difficulties. According to one source he went to Northern Germany, and took a job as a schoolmaster at Herrnhut, Saxony. There he remained in the service of the Evangelical Brotherhood until the turn of the century. After which, so it is said, he went to Ireland to join a revolt, but was captured by the English and imprisoned in the Tower.

However this may be, in 1810 he was back again in Germany, living at New Wied, on the Rhine. When Marshal

Bernadotte was on his way to his new country, Lilliehorn, who was now calling himself Bergheim, sought him out at Hamburg. In a written petition in which he lauded all the Crown Prince's many good qualities and at the same time blackened the memory of Gustaf III, Lilliehorn requested permission to visit his native country on urgent financial business. Informed of Lilliehorn's antecedents, however, Bernadotte, that ex-republican general, flung the petition away from him. Now he was a Swedish Crown Prince. And his duty was to the Swedish Royal Family.

But even if Lilliehorn never got permission to go to Sweden and collect his inheritance after the death of his brother, Adjutant-General Pehr Ulrik Lilliehorn, his affairs soon improved. Marrying a wealthy Fraülein von Linden he was able to lead a pleasant life until his death at Bonn, in 1820.

INDEX